LIGHTHOUSES

75 MOST MAGNIFICENT LIGHTHOUSES

AN OCEANA BOOK

This book is produced by
Oceana Books
6 Blundell Street
London
N7 9BH

ISBN-13: 978-1-84573-400-8

QUMLGHT

Editor: Richard Wiles
Designer: Kevin Collier
Picture Researcher: Ildikó Egervári

Printed in Singapore by
Star Standard Industries (Pte) Ltd.

LIGHTHOUSES

75 MOST MAGNIFICENT LIGHTHOUSES

Ian Penberthy

Oceana

CONTENTS

Guiding lights

The purpose of a lighthouse is to display a light as an aid to navigation at sea. They are used to mark hazardous coastlines, submerged rocks and shoals, and the safe channels into and out of harbors. Although many lighthouses remain in the world, their numbers are declining thanks to modern navigation aids, such as the Global Positioning System (GPS).

The earliest nautical lights were established thousands of years ago, as beacon fires on prominent headlands, or candles displayed in the windows of buildings. In the eighteenth century, wick lamps were developed and used in conjunction with parabolic reflectors to concentrate the light. Various types of oil were used as fuel, depending on the location of the lighthouse, such as whale oil, olive oil, and colza oil. Kerosene was employed during the nineteenth century, being replaced in the early 1900s by compressed acetylene gas and electricity.

To make the lamps more visible, lenses were developed to concentrate the light rays. The most important of these was the Fresnel lens, invented in the early nineteenth century by Augustin-Jean Fresnel.

Frequently, lenses were required to rotate so that the light could sweep the ocean. To make them easy to turn, they were floated on mercury. Initially, rotation was achieved with a clockwork mechanism that had to be wound by the keeper, often every three or four hours. With the advent of electrification, motors were installed. Nowadays, many automated lighthouses have flashing strobe lights, such as those used at airports.

Until the early twentieth century, lighthouses had to be tended by keepers, who led a lonely, isolated life. They would trim the lamp wicks, top up the oil, keep the lenses clean, operate the rotating mechanisms, and sound fog signals. Eventually, methods were developed of automating the process, particularly once an electricity supply became available. Today, many lighthouses use solar power to produce electricity.

Types of Lighthouse

Fortress tower:	The earliest lights were often positioned on top of lookout towers belonging to fortresses or other tall buildings so that the light could be seen from the farthest distance.
Offshore tower:	Towers were constructed directly on offshore rocks, on areas of shoal, or on caissons sunk on the seabed.
Onshore tower:	Those constructed onshore were normally shorter than offshore types, since they could be placed on higher ground.
Integral lighthouse:	Some offshore and onshore towers were combined with a keeper's dwelling.
Pile lighthouse:	In areas of shallow water, where the seabed was mud or sand, a series of narrow, wooden or iron poles, known as piles, were driven into the bed and a building erected on top. This accommodated the keeper and supported the lantern on its roof.

Far left: *An offshore lighthouse had to withstand the unbridled rage of the sea. Inaccessible other than by boat, many older lighthouses, such as Longships in Cornwall, England, were fitted with helipads to allow the keepers to be kept supplied, or, after automation, to enable access by maintenance crews.*

Top right: *The "vippefyr," or bascule light was a navigational aid used in Scandinavia during the eighteenth century, such as this replica in Skagen, Denmark. The basket was filled with wood or coal, then ignited and hauled aloft by a lever.*

Right: *A pile lighthouse, such as Low Lighthouse in Burnham-on-Sea, England, comprises stout posts driven into the seabed, on which the building is mounted.*

Right: *Onshore towers were built on high ground close to the water's edge, where their light could indicate the presence of a promontory, or, in conjunction with other beacons, the entrance to a bay or inlet. Ancillary buildings were built around the tower, providing a dwelling for the keeper, such as the classic lighthouse at Portland Head in Maine, USA.*

Right: *Thinner than a conventional lens, the Fresnel lens concentrated the light so that it could be seen over a great distance. Fresnel lenses were made in various sizes and strengths, known as "orders." First-order lenses were largest and most powerful, while sixth-order lenses were smallest. The magnificent first-order lens of Cordouan Lighthouse, France, dates from 1854 and is large enough to stand inside. It remains in use today and has a range of 27 miles (43km).*

Cordouan Lighthouse

Gironde Estuary, France

• **The Cordouan Lighthouse marks the entrance to the mighty Gironde River on the Atlantic coast of France, helping to guide shipping on its way upriver to the port of Bordeaux.**

• **This grand lighthouse is the oldest in France and one of the most famous in the world.**

• **The tower is known locally as *"Le roi des phares, le phare des rois"* (the king of lighthouses, the lighthouse of kings).**

The Gironde River enters the Atlantic Ocean through the Bay of Biscay, on the west coast of France. Upstream lies the ancient and busy port of Bordeaux, and for many centuries the river and its estuary have been a bustling waterway. For much of that time, the Cordouan Lighthouse has helped guide shipping on its way. This historic tower stands at the mouth of the river on a sandbar that, for most of the time, is submerged beneath the waves.

It is said that Charlemagne ordered a beacon to be established near the site of the lighthouse in the early ninth century. Then it was a low peninsula, but any evidence of the ancient light has been washed away. It is known that a stone tower with a beacon fire was erected in 1360.

In 1584, King Henri III instructed the engineer Louis de Foix to construct a new lighthouse, but by that time the peninsula had become an island, making construction extremely difficult, such that the elaborate tower with its spectacular architecture was not completed until 1611. By then, the island had also disappeared.

The three-story, cylindrical tower contained a magnificent entrance hall, an apartment on the second floor called the "King's Chamber," and a chapel complete with stained-glass windows on the third floor. Above that, a domed roof covered a beacon fire. In 1782, the open fire was replaced by oil lamps and a reflector, but the lighthouse was not tall enough, and during a renovation program carried out between 1786 and 1790, a conical tower was added, increasing the height to 223ft (68m).

Far left: *Standing on a sandbar that is exposed at low water, Cordouan Lighthouse is probably the grandest lighthouse in the world, having a bedroom fit for a king and its own private chapel. The base of the tower is protected from the pounding of the sea by a 134.5ft (41m) diameter donut-shaped bastion that contains living accommodation for the keepers together with freshwater tanks.*

Above right: *A stone causeway leading to the lighthouse is revealed when the tide recedes. Built on what was once a peninsula, the tower is now marooned 4 miles (7km) out to sea.*

Right: *The newer part of the tower extends upward from the decorative ring below the hooded windows. The magnificent first-order Fresnel lens housed in the lantern room dates from 1854 and is large enough to stand inside. It remains in use today and has a range of 27 miles (43km).*

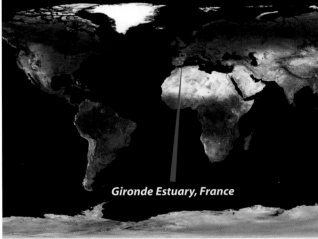

Gironde Estuary, France

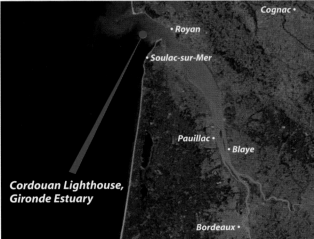

Cognac

Royan

Soulac-sur-Mer

Pauillac

Blaye

Cordouan Lighthouse, Gironde Estuary

Bordeaux

AN ILLUMINATING STORY

In 1823, Augustin-Jean Fresnel installed the first of his lenses at the Cordouan Lighthouse, in conjunction with an oil lamp of concentric wicks. The arrangement produced a light intensity that was far superior to anything seen before. He used the setup to perfect his lens design, which was soon in use around the world.

Cap de la Hague Lighthouse

Cotentin Peninsula, France

- **Cap de la Hague Lighthouse marks the northwestern tip of France's Cotentin Peninsula and the treacherous strait that runs between the peninsula and the British Channel Island of Alderney.**

- **For over 170 years, the lighthouse has helped guide shipping through some of the most dangerous waters in the world, protecting the lives of thousands of seafarers.**

- **The lighthouse is also known as the Goury Lighthouse, being named after a small fishing port nearby.**

The Cotentin Peninsula lies on the northwest coast of France, jutting out into the English Channel; at the northwestern tip is Cap de la Hague. The coast in this region is rugged and dangerous, while the seas are strewn with rocky outcrops that lie in wait for unwary seafarers. To the west of the peninsula are the Channel Islands, and the most northeastern of these is Alderney. This small island is separated from the Cotentin Peninsula by a 10-mile (16km) wide strait known as the Alderney Race, or Raz Blanchard in France. This notorious stretch of water contains the strongest tidal currents in Europe. These are produced by the Atlantic tidal surge building up in the Gulf of St. Malo to the south and then being forced through the narrow channel between Alderney and the French coast. As the tide recedes, the water is sucked back through. Adding to the disturbance is an uneven seabed.

Because of the large number of shipwrecks in this region, it was decided to erect a lighthouse at the tip of the Cotentin Peninsula, to warn eastbound vessels of its position and also to mark the northern end of the race. The building was designed by Charles Morice Felix de la Rue, chief engineer for the region of Cherbourg-Valognes. Work began on the 167ft (51m) high, round, granite tower in 1834 on a small, waveswept rock just off the coast known as the Gros-du-Raz. Many local people who knew the sea conditions around the rock considered the task to be impossible, but de la Rue triumphed, and the lighthouse was commissioned in 1837.

Far left: *The part of the French coast on which Cap de la Hague Lighthouse stands saw heavy fighting during World War II, and many lighthouses were destroyed. This sturdy stone structure survived, however, and continues its vital task. The light was electrified in 1971 and fully automated in 1990, when the last keepers were withdrawn.*

Above right: *Cap de la Hague Lighthouse stands defiant against some of the most treacherous seas, and has saved many lives in the past. However, as testament to the difficulty of its task, on the point across from the lighthouse is a monument to some of the seafarers who have not been so lucky.*

Right: *The life of the lighthouse keepers, marooned in the midst of such hostile conditions, must have been lonely and harsh, but now that the beacon has been automated it can carry on its lifesaving duties for many years to come, a solitary sentinel in the broiling sea.*

Cotentin Peninsula, France

Cap de la Hague Lighthouse, Cotentin Peninsula

Alderney • Cherbourg
Guernsey
Jersey • Créances
• Paimpol
Saint-Malo •

SMUGGLERS' DEN

In the past, the residents of the Cotentin Peninsula were looked upon as rogues and thieves, not entirely without good reason. The proximity of the Channel Islands led to the rise of a flourishing smuggling industry, most notably in textiles during the seventeenth century and tobacco in the nineteenth century. Moreover, before the construction of lighthouses, the many ships wrecked on the fearsome coast during stormy weather provided a constant bounty in washed-up cargoes.

Beachy Head Lighthouse

East Sussex, England

- **The lighthouse at Beachy Head was built to warn mariners to keep away from tall, dangerous chalk cliffs that project out into the English Channel.**
- **The stone tower dates from the early part of the last century, although it is said that a light was displayed at the top of the cliffs as early as 1670.**
- **The lighthouse is located at sea level on a rocky promontory, and for most of the time it is surrounded by the sea.**

Just to the west of the seaside town of Eastbourne, in the English county of East Sussex, the ground rises rapidly to become steep chalk cliffs. These create a headland that juts out into the busy waters of the English Channel. The cliffs are the tallest sea cliffs in Britain, rising to 530ft (162m) above sea level.

At the tip of the headland is Beachy Head, a noted landmark for mariners, but also a dangerous one. In recognition of this, the first lighthouse marking the cliffs was built in 1828 by James Walker. Known as the Belle Toute Lighthouse, it was a 46ft (14m) high, round stone tower erected on the top of the cliffs. Unfortunately, because it was so high, there were times when it was shrouded in low cloud and its light could not be seen. Even so, it remained in operation until the end of the century, when it was abandoned.

In 1902, a new lighthouse marking Beachy Head was brought into operation, and that is the structure that remains today. Positioned 541ft (165m) to seaward of the cliff base, it is a 141ft (43m) high, tapering, round stone tower with a lantern on top. It took two years to build, requiring the construction of a coffer dam, and a cablecar to ferry men and materials from the top of the cliffs to the site. The tower was constructed from 3,660 tons of Cornish granite.

Painted in red and white stripes, Beachy Head Lighthouse was manned by three keepers until it was fully automated in 1983. Its light produces two white flashes every twenty seconds and can be seen from 26 miles (42km) out to sea.

Far Left: *Dwarfed by the massive chalk cliffs that cut into the English Channel, the Beachy Head Lighthouse was built at the beginning of the twentieth century under the supervision of Sir Thomas Matthews, chief engineer of Trinity House, the organization set up to run all of England's lighthouses.*

Top right: *At low tide, the rocky peninsula on which the lighthouse stands is exposed, but for much of the time, the tower is surrounded by the sea. It is a well-known local landmark, and taking a cruise around the lighthouse is a popular pastime for those vacationing in the nearby seaside town of Eastbourne.*

Right: *As darkness falls over Beachy Head, the lighthouse sends out its bright, warning beam, helping vessels to keep clear of the dangerous cliffs.*

Beachy Head, East Sussex, England

London · ENGLAND · Dover · Calais · Hastings · Portsmouth

Beachy Head Lighthouse, East Sussex · FRANCE

WHAT'S IN A NAME?

The name Beachy Head actually has nothing to do with a beach. Instead, it is a corruption of the old Norman name for the headland, "Beauchef," which means "Beautiful Headland." This dates from the time of Norman rule in England, which began in the late eleventh century. By 1317, it had become "Beaucheif," but by 1724, it was known consistently as Beachy Head.

The original Belle Toute Lighthouse eventually became a private home; in 1999, it was moved 50ft (17m) back from the cliff edge, as it was in danger of toppling over.

La Vieille Lighthouse

Finistère, France

- **One of the most well-known French lighthouses, La Vieille sits atop a rock off the northwestern tip of France known as La Gorlebella, which means "the farthest rock" in the Breton language.**

- **La Vieille lighthouse is one of several that mark dangerous rocks and areas of strong currents in this region, acting as an aid to navigation in the strait known as the Raz de Sein.**

- **Construction of the lighthouse was a major feat, since access to the rock could only be gained at a specific period of the moon, when the currents and tides were at their calmest.**

Situated in an isolated spot in the rough seas off the Pointe du Raz, La Vieille Lighthouse was nearly never built at all because of the dangerous conditions that exist around La Gorlebella. Ten years passed between the first feasibility studies and the light being brought into operation.

In November 1861, the French Commission for Lighthouses proposed that a study be made of La Gorlebella rock to determine whether or not a lighthouse could be built there. Before it could be carried out, however, a lack of funds and commitments to other lighthouse projects led to its postponement. Ten years later, in 1872, the idea was raised and postponed again, an official of the Lighthouse Service admitting that the difficulties of actually getting onto the rock could see the project being abandoned altogether.

In 1879, however, landings were made on La Gorlebella, allowing the rock itself, the local currents, and the ease of docking to be assessed. Violent currents surround the rock almost constantly, and the few sheltered landing points are accessible for short periods of time only. In fact, the rock can only be approached from the north, and then only for three days either side of the quarter-moon. Despite this, local fishermen managed to establish mooring points and a simple stone dock was built. In the following year, the landing platform was extended to allow building materials to be offloaded. Although getting on and off the rock was difficult, working there was not as dangerous as some other lighthouse projects. The rock rises 46ft (14m) out of the sea at high tide and was large enough for a substantial foundation to be built. Work finally began on the lighthouse itself in 1881, the masons spending about five months of each year on the task. The construction was completed in 1887, and the light was illuminated for the first time on September 15 of that year.

Far left: *Surrounded by jagged rocks and rough seas, La Vieille Lighthouse was constructed from gray granite blocks quarried from the nearby Ile de Sein, while coated cinder blocks of blue granite were used for the corners and base of the tower. The shape of the tower was chosen so that it would not be confused with the nearby Tévennec Lighthouse.*

Top right: *: The 89ft (27m) high, square tower is topped by crenellations, a gallery, and a lantern, the light showing white, red, or green, depending on the direction from which it is seen.*

Right: *Perched high on the rock known as La Gorlebella and looking out over the choppy waters of the Raz de Sein, La Vieille Lighthouse has a sturdy appearance and seems ready for anything the ocean is able to throw at it.*

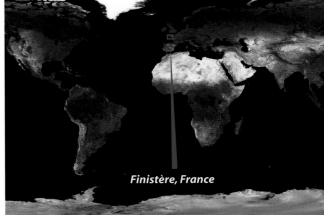

Finistère, France

La Vieille Lighthouse, Finistère

- Morlaix
- Brest
- Saint-Malo
- Quimper
- Rennes
- Vannes

WORKERS REVOLT
La Vieille Lighthouse was the second to last lighthouse in France to be automated (in 1995). The changeover was delayed by the fact that the lighthouse keepers refused to carry out the necessary conversion work, since it would mean the loss of their livelihood.

Eddystone Lighthouse

English Channel, England

- **The most famous lighthouse in England, Eddystone Lighthouse stands on a wave-lashed rock off the southwest coast.**
- **The late-nineteenth-century lighthouse marks a dangerous reef in the English Channel.**
- **This was the first English lighthouse to be fully automated, and it is monitored from a control center 270 miles (435km) away.**

Eddystone Lighthouse stands on a treacherous reef in the English Channel, about 13 miles (21km) southwest of the busy port of Plymouth, a major naval base. Before the first lighthouse was built, the "Stone," as it is known locally, took a heavy toll on ships, with as many as fifty being wrecked each year.

The first lighthouse was an octagonal wooden tower constructed by Henry Winstanley, a merchant who had lost two ships on the Eddystone. Illuminated by candles, it had to be rebuilt within a year. Four years later, it was swept away during a severe storm, along with the keepers and Winstanley himself.

The third lighthouse was a round wooden tower, braced internally by a ship's mast. Designed by John Rudyerd, a silk merchant, and erected in 1709, it survived until 1755, when it caught fire. While fighting the fire, the keepers were showered with molten lead from the lantern roof, and one of them actually swallowed some. Although this was not believed at the time, after he died twelve days later, a postmortem revealed a piece of lead weighing over 7oz (0.2kg) in his stomach.

By now the value of the Eddystone Lighthouse was appreciated by seafarers who plied the English Channel, and a lightship was stationed at the Eddystone until a new stone tower could be built. Completed in 1759, it was designed by John Smeaton, using an oak tree as his inspiration. It was constructed from granite blocks held together with dovetail joints and quick-drying cement of Smeaton's own invention. In the 1870s, cracks appeared in the rock on which the lighthouse stood and it had to be abandoned.

The current, fourth, lighthouse, a round stone tower, was subsequently built, and was first lit in 1882.

Far left: *The present lighthouse was built just to the southeast of the remaining stub of John Smeaton's previous structure, being commissioned in 1882. The 168ft (51m) high, round tower was designed by James Douglass and incorporated refinements of Smeaton's ideas. When the helipad is not in use by maintenance crews, the deck becomes crowded with seabirds.*

Top right: *To ensure greater strength, larger stone blocks were used, not only with dovetail end joints, but also dovetails between the courses. When the tower was automated in 1982, a helipad was added above the lantern to provide access for maintenance crews.*

Right: *The present lantern has a white light that flashes every ten seconds, and its light is visible from a range of 25.3 miles (41km). A fog signal delivers three blasts every 60 seconds.*

English Channel, England

Eddystone Lighthouse, English Channel

ENGLAND · London
· Bristol
· Portsmouth
· Exeter
· Plymouth
English Channel
· Falmouth
· Cherbourg
FRANCE

FLAME OF HOPE

The first Eddystone Lighthouse was built at a time when England was at war with France, and one day a French warship seized Winstanley and his men. Upon hearing of this, the French king, Louis XIV, ordered their release, saying, "France is at war with England, not with humanity." Thus, the lighthouse achieved international importance.

The top portion of John Smeaton's lighthouse was carefully dismantled and shipped to Plymouth, where it was reerected as a memorial to the pioneering engineer. The stump of the tower remains on the Eddystone.

La Corbière Lighthouse

Jersey, Channel Islands

- **The lighthouse that stands on the rocky headland of La Corbière marks a treacherous area of sea off the southwestern tip of the island of Jersey in the English Channel Islands.**

- **Dating from the late nineteenth century, La Corbière Lighthouse was the first in Britain to be built from reinforced concrete.**

- **The lighthouse is a well-known landmark in the islands and is depicted on a Jersey banknote and coin.**

The Channel Islands lie in the Gulf of Saint Malo on the southern edge of the English Channel, just off the northwest coast of France. Despite this, they are British territory. There are four main islands: Jersey, Guernsey, Alderney, and Sark. Of these, Jersey is the largest.

The seas around the Channel Islands are rocky and fraught with danger for unwary mariners. One of the worst areas lies off La Corbière, a rugged peninsula at the southwestern tip of Jersey. There, submerged rocks and a wide tidal range have caused many vessels to come to grief in the past, among them the mail steamer *Express* on September 20, 1859.

In an attempt to reduce the number of sinkings, it was decided to erect a lighthouse at La Corbière. Designed by Sir John Goode, the 62ft (19m) high, round, conical tower was constructed from reinforced concrete blocks, a first for Britain. The stout tower stands on the end of the peninsula, but is cut off from the mainland at high tide, a causeway being revealed as the water recedes. Originally, the lantern was equipped with a vaporized kerosene lamp, but this was replaced by a 1,000 watt bulb when an electricity supply was provided in the mid-1960s. The light, which is 119ft (36m) above sea level, has a range of 18 miles (29km) and shows white or red depending on the direction from which it is seen.

When first commissioned, the lighthouse had a bell and explosive fog warner. Subsequently, this arrangement was replaced by a foghorn operated by compressed air, and then by an electric horn.

Far left: *The sturdy looking La Corbière Lighthouse has marked the dangerous headland for over 130 years. For those sailing to Jersey's harbor of St. Helier, rounding the promontory and its brilliant white lighthouse means that they are nearing journey's end, but that they may also be in for the roughest part of their passage because of the turbulent waters.*

Above right: *La Corbière is a popular spot for watching splendid sunsets. As the dusk falls, the lighthouse's lantern begins to glow, throwing out its protective beam.*

Right: *The lighthouse is perched atop a rugged, rocky outcrop that is a tidal island; at low tide, it is possible to walk to the lighthouse, although this has led to visitors becoming trapped as the water rises.*

Jersey, Channel Islands

La Corbière Lighthouse, Jersey

Cherbourg

Guernsey

St. Helier

Créances

Paimpol

Saint-Malo

FRANCE

WARTIME ROLE

During the German occupation of the Channel Islands in World War II, La Corbière Lighthouse was only lit when German ships needed to pass around the rugged headland. An extra story was added to the lighthouse during the war to provide accommodation for the troops stationed there. After the war, this was removed and the lighthouse restored to its original condition.

Needles Lighthouse

Isle of Wight, England

- **Needles Lighthouse marks a narrow chalky peninsula that extends into the English Channel from the western end of the Isle of Wight, an island off the south coast of England.**

- **Dating from the mid-nineteenth century, the present round stone tower replaced an earlier lighthouse that had been built on top of the adjacent cliffs.**

- **Manned until as recently as 1994, the lighthouse is now fully automated and controlled from the Trinity House operations center 150 miles (240km) away at Harwich, on England's east coast.**

Far left: *From the shore, Needles Lighthouse is partially obscured by the imposing chalk stacks that it guards. The helipad was erected on top of the tower in 1987 to make changing and supplying the crews much easier. Seven years later, however, the light was automated and the crews withdrawn.*

Top right: *Set against the deep blue of the sea, the stark white chalk cliffs and the brightly painted lighthouse sparkle in the sunlight. This image has become a symbol of the Isle of Wight and features on many souvenirs sold on the island.*

The Needles is a line of three jagged chalk stacks that rise out of the sea in the western approaches to the Isle of Wight; to seaward, there is a shifting shoal of pebbles just below the waves known as the Shingles. These two geological formations have always been hazards to shipping heading into the sound known as the Solent on their way to the harbors of Southampton and Portsmouth.

In 1785, at the urging of merchants and shipowners, Trinity House, the body that oversees England's lighthouses, began construction of a lighthouse on top of the cliffs adjacent to the Needles. This was completed in the following year, and the light shone out for the first time on September 29 of that year. Unfortunately, the elevated position meant that the light was 472ft (144m) above sea level, and it was often obscured by low cloud and sea mist, making it of limited use to mariners.

Far left: *More than 1,600 colorful yachts race from the Royal Yacht Squadron startline off Cowes near Needles Lighthouse in the annual J.P. Morgan Round the Island Race 2006 on June 3, 2006.*

Despite its shortcomings, the first Needles Lighthouse continued in operation until 1859, when Trinity House began construction of a new lighthouse on the most seaward of the Needles rocks, much closer to sea level. This is the lighthouse that remains in use today. Designed by James Walker, who was responsible for many other English lighthouses, the cylindrical granite tower is 109ft (33.25m) high and was erected on a stepped base, shaped to break up the waves and stop them from pounding on the base of the structure. At the bottom of the tower, the walls are a massive 3.5ft (1.07m) thick, although this reduces toward the top, where they are 2ft (0.61m) thick. Below the tower, storerooms were cut into the chalk. The total cost of this new aid to navigation was $39,750.

One of the problems associated with all lighthouses on remote rocks is being able to land and take off their crews, and keep them supplied. Trinity House solved this difficulty at the Needles by building a helipad on top of the tower in 1987. On December 8, 1994, however, the last crew was withdrawn when the lighthouse was automated.

Isle of Wight, England

Needles Lighthouse, Isle of Wight

Southampton
Portsmouth
Bournemouth
Isle of Wight
Exeter
English Channel

LOT'S WIFE

None of the three chalk outcrops that comprise the Needles is needle-like in appearance. The group got its name because at one time there was a fourth column of chalk, which was very tall and narrow. Known as Lot's Wife, this collapsed during a storm in 1764.

Longships Lighthouse

Land's End, England

- **Longships Lighthouse marks a dangerous area of rocks that lies just off Land's End in the far southwest of the mainland of England.**
- **Built in the late nineteenth century, the lighthouse has prevented many a ship from being dashed to pieces on the surrounding rocks.**
- **The present lighthouse replaced an earlier tower that was not tall enough to be seen above the stormy seas that often overwhelmed it.**

The rugged peninsula known as Land's End forms the far southwestern extremity of the English mainland. The seas around this headland are peppered with treacherous rocks that have sealed the fate of many a vessel in stormy seas or poor visibility, especially before the construction of lighthouses to warn of their presence. One such group of rocks is the Longships, which lies about a mile (1.6km) to the west of Land's End.

In the late eighteenth century, Trinity House, the English lighthouse service, made plans to construct beacons that would mark the presence of the rocks around Land's End. For the Longships, a lease was granted to a Lieutenant Henry Smith, allowing him to construct a lighthouse there. The structure was built on Carn Bras, the largest of the rocks and completed in 1791. The three-story tower was 40ft (12m) high, being topped by a wooden and copper lantern. In 1795, Smith was declared unfit to manage the tower, and Trinity House took over its operation.

In stormy seas, however, the lighthouse was often inundated by the waves, obscuring the light. This led to its replacement by the present 115ft (35m) high, round granite tower, which was commissioned in 1875. Designed by the Trinity House engineer Sir James Douglass, the new structure was tall enough for its light to be seen in even the roughest of seas. Even so, this did not prevent the steamship *Blue Jacket* from running onto the rocks on a clear night in 1898, nearly demolishing the lighthouse in the process.

Gaining access to such exposed lighthouses is often hazardous, and is impossible in heavy seas. Consequently, a helipad was added to the top of the Longships Lighthouse, although since the beacon was automated in 1988, this is only rarely used.

Far left: *Perched on a small rock just off the southwest tip of England, Land's End, the Longships Lighthouse is vulnerable to the full fury of the ocean, but has withstood the pounding waves for over 130 years, a tribute to its design and the skills of its builders.*

Above right: *The jagged Longships Rocks laid claim to many ships over the years before a light was established there; even then, the treacherous reef was capable of trapping the unwary mariners.*

Right: *Longships Lighthouse stands defiant against the huge waves that crash around its base. It is easy to see why the original 40ft (12m) tower was not high enough.*

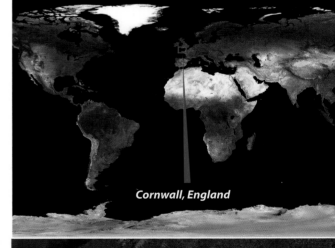

Cornwall, England

Longships Lighthouse, Land's End

A HARD LIFE

Life in the original Longships Lighthouse was tough for the keepers. Two would man the lighthouse for a month, then spend a month ashore before going back again. While on duty, they would be paid a small sum and receive free food, but on shore they were expected to fend for themselves and were forced to take on other work to make ends meet.

Harbor of Refuge Lighthouse

Cape Henlopen, USA

• **Standing completely exposed on the end of a breakwater at the mouth of the Delaware Bay, the Harbor of Refuge Lighthouse has endured many a battering from Atlantic storms.**

• **Known as a "sparkplug" lighthouse because of its resemblance to the shape of a car's sparkplug, the lighthouse marks the breakwater that protects the National Harbor of Refuge, a place where ships can ride out stormy weather.**

• **The lighthouse was one of a pair of beacons that marked both ends of the breakwater, but the eastern light no longer exists.**

Before the creation of the Harbor of Refuge, there was no natural safe harbor between New York and the capes of Chesapeake Bay. Ships encountering the intense storms that occur in this region of the North Atlantic had nowhere to run from the perilous weather. Thus, in 1825, Congress authorized the construction of a breakwater at Cape Henlopen to form an area of sheltered water. It was not completed until 1869, however, and soon it became clear that the harbor was not deep enough for the latest merchant and naval vessels. Consequently, it was decided to build an outer breakwater to encompass deeper water. This was completed in 1892 and marked by temporary beacons, but within a year they had been swept away by the sea.

In 1906, a permanent lighthouse was built at the western end of the breakwater. Based on a cylindrical iron foundation, it was a three-story, hexagonal wooden tower. Completed in 1907, the structure was soon being battered by stormy seas, the waves often crashing over the top. In 1918, a severe storm moved it 2in (5cm) off its foundations; two years later, it was dislodged again.

Condemned as uninhabitable, the old lighthouse was dismantled in 1925 and work began on a replacement, the present 76ft (23m) high, conical tower. Constructed from cast iron lined with brick and erected on a caisson filled with reinforced concrete, the new structure was deemed strong enough to withstand the Atlantic storms.

Far left: *Exposed to the full force of Atlantic storms, the Harbor of Refuge Lighthouse has been tested severely. It has been shaken by hurricane-force winds, while windows have been broken by the waves, on one occasion causing partial flooding of the interior. A ship even collided with the caisson in 1986. Throughout, it has stood defiant. An array of solar panels provides the necessary power to keep its batteries fully charged.*

Top right: *Today, the lighthouse is under the charge of the Delaware River and Bay Lighthouse Foundation, a non-profit organization, which offers visitors seasonal tours of the historic tower.*

Right: *The lighthouse stands in a vulnerable position at the end of the Harbor of Refuge breakwater at the mouth of the Delaware Bay. The poor condition of the breakwater has given cause for concern about the lighthouse's future.*

Cape Henlopen, USA

Harbor of Refuge Lighthouse, Cape Henlopen

BENDING THE RULES

The lonely life of the men manning the Harbor of Refuge Lighthouse was often brightened by the arrival of fishing vessels, whose crews would pass them fresh fish or lobsters. Even beer would be delivered in this way, although this was strictly against regulations. The appearance of a Coast Guard vessel would provoke a mad scurry to hide the contraband quickly among the rocks of the breakwater until the vessel had left.

St. Catherine's Oratory

Isle of Wight, England

Far left: *Unusually, the octagonal exterior of the St. Catherine's Oratory Lighthouse conceals a square interior. The historic, rugged, stone tower has stood unmolested high above the English Channel for almost 700 years.*

- **The ancient St. Catherine's Oratory Lighthouse is perched high up on the top of St. Catherine's Point, a chalk headland at the extreme southern tip of the Isle of Wight, overlooking the English Channel.**
- **The medieval tower is the second oldest lighthouse in England, being predated by a Roman structure farther to the east at Dover.**
- **Because of its distinctive shape, the lighthouse is popularly known locally as the "Pepper Pot."**

The Isle of Wight is a diamond-shaped island lying off the south coast of England in the English Channel. The southern tip of the island, known as St. Catherine's Point, is a 785ft (240m) high chalk cliff that looms above the long, shallow Chale Bay to the west. On top of the cliff stands one of England's oldest lighthouse structures, St. Catherine's Oratory.

The history of the medieval lighthouse is shrouded in the mists of time, and the truth probably will never be known. However, the popularly accepted story is that it was built by a local landowner, Walter de Godeton, as a penance for stealing a cargo of wine, destined for a French monastery, from a ship that had been wrecked in Chale Bay in 1313.

The beacon tower was erected on the western elevation of the existing oratory, which housed the monks who would tend the fire and pray for shipwrecked sailors. According to the story, the work was completed in 1328, and the beacon remained in use until the mid-sixteenth century, when Henry VIII fell out with the Roman Catholic Church and dissolved the monasteries.

Another account, which is similar in many aspects, has it that while de Godeton was indeed fined for stealing wine from a wrecked ship in 1313, in fact the lighthouse already existed at that time, having been repaired in 1312. That said, the tower stood on de Godeton's land, so it is likely that he was required to maintain it.

Top right: *Not a medieval attempt at spaceflight, even though the buttresses and conical roof do make the tower look like a stone rocket. The oratory itself, now vanished apart from traces of its walls at ground level, was originally attached to the lighthouse. Its pitched roofline can still be seen on the side of the tower that is pierced by doorways on the first two of the tower's four stories.*

Right: *Eight narrow openings surround the top of the tower and would have allowed the light from the beacon fire to shine out into the night, warning mariners to keep clear of the dangerous headland. As with many early lighthouses, the fire was maintained by monks.*

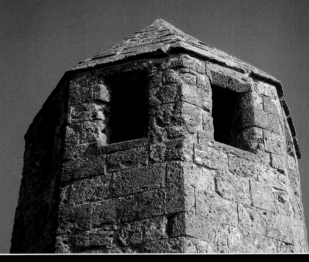

Isle of Wight, England

St. Catherine's Oratory, Isle of Wight

- Bristol
- Southampton
- Cowes
- Portsmouth
- Bournemouth
- Shanklin

PEPPER AND SALT

After the old tower on St. Catherine's Point was abandoned, there were a number of shipwrecks in Chale Bay. The area even became known locally as the "Bay of Death." Eventually, in 1785, work began on a new lighthouse not far from the old tower. However, it was soon realized that because of the height of the cliff, the light would often be obscured by fog and low cloud, so the project was abandoned. The unfinished tower was soon nicknamed the "Salt Shaker" by locals. In 1837, a new lighthouse was built below the cliffs, about a mile (1.6km) to the east.

Alnes Lighthouse

Godøy, Norway

- **Marking the entrance to a small fishing harbor on the Norwegian island of Godøy, Alnes Lighthouse doubles as an aid to navigation and a local cultural center.**
- **The wooden tower has been unmanned since 1982, when the light was automated, but today it contains a small museum and art gallery. It is one of the most visited lighthouses in Norway, and it is preserved under the Norwegian Cultural Heritage Act.**
- **The present lighthouse is the second to stand on the spot, the first having been built in 1852.**

As is the case on many islands, fishing makes a major contribution to the economy of the island of Godøy, located off the west coast of Norway and one of a group of islands that make up the municipality of Giske. In the northwest of the island is the small village and harbor of Alnes. There, as in so many fishing communities, the safe return of the fleet in bad weather or at night is of major concern to everyone. To this end, a lighthouse was built in 1853 to guide the boats home. This remained in service for over twenty years until 1876, when a new tower was built. That lighthouse remains in use today and has rarely been out of action since it was first commissioned. It is the predominant feature of the village.

The historic and unusual Alnes Lighthouse is a 75ft (23m) high, square wooden tower with tapering sides, topped by the lantern and gallery. The tower has clapboard siding and is painted white with two broad red stripes to make it distinguishable when viewed from out to sea. Built alongside the tower is a small wooden cottage for the lighthouse keeper, together with a boathouse. The lighthouse was manned until 1982, when it was automated, and it remains an aid to navigation. Its light flashes twice every eight seconds, showing white, red, or green, depending on the direction from which it is seen.

Since 1993, the lighthouse and the adjacent buildings have been used as a local and regional cultural center. Not only do they house a museum and art gallery, but also a cafe and gift shop. They are a popular tourist attraction and easily visited, since the islands of Giske are connected to the mainland by undersea tunnels and a bridge. The lighthouse is maintained by Giske Municipality.

Far left: *Unusually for such a high tower, Alnes Lighthouse is constructed from wood, but since it is onshore and protected from the sea, the material was a practical choice. It looms high above the surrounding buildings and is a well-known landmark on the island of Godøy.*

Top right: *The tower is surmounted by an octagonal gallery that surrounds the iron lantern. On top of the conical roof is a circular vent that allows excess heat produced by the lamp to escape from the lantern room.*

Right: *Etched sharply against the fading blue of an evening sky, Alnes Lighthouse, in its distinctive red and white bands, stands ready to guide the local fishing fleet home to the small harbor of Alnes.*

Gødoy, Norway

Alnes Lighthouse, Gødoy

Haram

Herøy

Vanylven

Florø

A STEEP CLIMB

Guided tours are offered of the Alnes Lighthouse and keeper's cottage, and visitors can climb to the gallery at the top of the tower to obtain fine views of the surrounding island, across to the mainland in the east, and out over the Atlantic to the west. They need to be fit, though, since there are around a hundred steep steps to negotiate, and the last few are little more than a ladder.

Bald Head Island Lighthouse

North Carolina, USA

- **The Bald Head Island Lighthouse was built to mark the entrance of the Cape Fear River on the east coast of the United States in North Carolina. It is the second lighthouse to mark this spot and dates from the early nineteenth century.**

- **Known affectionately as "Old Baldy," the lighthouse is the oldest lighthouse in North Carolina and the oldest brick-built lighthouse in the United States.**

- **The lighthouse remained in operation until 1935, although it was equipped with a radio beacon during World War II as an aid to the U.S. Navy.**

Bald Head Island is actually part of Smith Island, which is crisscrossed by creeks and inlets, breaking up the land into a series of smaller "islands." To the southeast is a large area of shifting sandbars just below the waves known as Frying Pan Shoals. These dangerous waters led early seafarers to dub the region Cape Fear, a name that was also applied to the river that empties into the ocean at this point.

In 1794, to mark the entrance channel to the river for ships heading to the port of Wilmington several miles upstream, a lighthouse was built on the west side of Bald Head Island, but coastal erosion soon made it apparent that the structure was in the wrong place. As a result, in 1814, Congress authorized the erection of a new lighthouse farther inland. This was completed in 1817.

When commissioned originally, the light had the equivalent strength of a harbor light, but mariners complained that it was of no use for guiding ships around the treacherous Frying Pan Shoals. The Lighthouse Board asked for funding to raise the height of the lighthouse and install a stronger light, but this was refused by Congress. Instead a lightship was stationed at the shoals.

Today, the lighthouse is maintained by the Old Baldy Foundation and is open to visitors.

Far left: *The 91ft (28m) high Bald Head Island Lighthouse was built of stucco rendered brick to the standard federal octagonal design, measuring 36ft (11m) wide at the base and tapering to 14.5ft (4.4m) at the top. The "pepper-pot" shape is actually quite efficient aerodynamically and is capable of withstanding Category 3 hurricanes. The mottled appearance of the lighthouse is the result of patchwork repairs to the stucco.*

Top right: *Today, the lighthouse is open as a tourist attraction, while the replica 1850s keeper's cottage provides a home for the Smith Island Museum, which charts over 400 years of the region's maritime history. Visitors can climb the 112 wooden stairs to the top of the tower to obtain a panoramic view of the surrounding island and the ocean.*

Right: *The circular lantern was offset at the top of the tower to allow an access ladder to be installed. In 1985, the lighthouse was relit as an unofficial navigation aid.*

Outer Banks, North Carolina, USA

- Fayetteville

Jacksonville •   • Morehead City

• Wilmington

Bald Head Island Lighthouse, Bald Head Island

HURRICANE SHELTER

Bald Head Island gets its name from an area of bare sand dunes that have the appearance of a bald head when seen from out at sea. One legend has it that the vegetation was trampled away by pilots waiting on the shore for ships that needed guiding into the Cape Fear River.

On September 5, 1996, Hurricane Fran came ashore on the North Carolina coast. Although many residents had left Bald Head Island, a few remained, many of whom sought shelter in the lighthouse as the violent winds tore at their homes. The tower withstood the Category 3 hurricane, suffering only minor damage, making it one of the safest structures on the island.

Bremerhaven Rear Light

Bremerhaven, Germany

• The striking and elegant neogothic styling of the Bremerhaven Rear Light makes it a noted landmark in the busy German North Sea port, where it has operated since the mid-nineteenth century.

• Also known as the Bremerhaven Oberfeuer (high light), the lighthouse forms part of a range with the Bremerhaven Front Light, which does not benefit from the same extravagant architecture.

• The lighthouse stands at the entrance to a lock that opens into the basin known as Neuer Haven, and originally the lighthouse keepers were responsible for the lock's operation as well.

Far left: *Construction of the Bremerhaven Rear Light began in 1853, and the building was completed in 1855. It continued in operation as a manned lighthouse until 1942, when it was automated. An octagonal lantern with a decorative finial and weathervane tops it off. The ornate iron bracket protruding just below the lantern was used originally for hoisting storm signals.*

Bremerhaven is located at the mouth of the River Weser, which flows into the North Sea on Germany's west coast. Today, it is the fourth largest container port in Europe and also a major European gateway for the import and export of cars. Surprisingly, it is a relatively young port and city, having been established in 1827, although prior to that, there were several villages on the islands in the river's marshy estuary. The land was purchased to provide a port for the city of Bremen, 31 miles (50km) upstream, where the existing harbor was becoming unusable due to extensive silting.

After Bremerhaven's locks and port area had been established, a local Bremen architect, Simon Loschen, was commissioned to design a lighthouse that would guide ships into the harbor. An enthusiast for gothic styling, Loschen gave full rein to his passion and created a lighthouse structure like no other. Originally, a three-story building was attached to the side of the tower to provide quarters for the lighthouse and lock keepers. This was built in the same eyecatching style, and from a distance, the entire structure had an almost church-like appearance. Unfortunately, the keepers' quarters were destroyed by bombing during World War II.

Surprisingly, the lighthouse survived the war, despite the fact that Bremerhaven was a major base of the German Navy and a large proportion of the city was flattened by the Allies.

Top right: *The lighthouse is an excellent example of the nineteenth-century fascination with gothic-style buildings and shows that structures that have a practical purpose can also make bold architectural statements.*

Right: *The 121ft (37m) high brick tower is square for a little over half its height, then octagonal, and finally round, being decorated with a wide variety of gothic adornments. The brickwork itself incorporates geometric features in different colored bricks.*

Bremerhaven, Germany

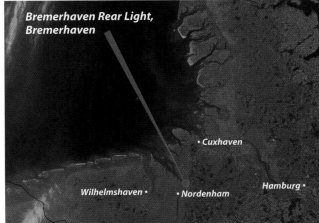

Bremerhaven Rear Light, Bremerhaven

• Cuxhaven

Wilhelmshaven •   • Nordenham   Hamburg •

CHALK AND CHEESE

Synchronized with the Bremerhaven Rear Light, the red and white banded Front Light does not boast the same extravagant architecture as its partner. The 26 m (85 ft) tower is a simple, conical, cast-iron structure with a gallery, and crowned by a large ball and spire.

Chania Lighthouse

Chania, Crete

- **The lighthouse that marks the harbor of the port of Chania, on the northwestern coast of Crete, is a striking, white stone tower that stands in stark contrast to the deep blue of the Mediterranean sea.**
- **Built in the mid-nineteenth century, the tower stands on the foundation of an earlier lighthouse that was constructed in the sixteenth century.**
- **While it is still active as an aid to navigation, the magnificent lighthouse has also become a major tourist attraction in the city.**

Chania is the second largest city in the Greek island of Crete, and its long history charts the rise and fall of civilizations in the eastern Mediterranean. Originally a Minoan city called Cydonia, it was largely occupied by Dorian Greek settlers around 1100 BC. The Romans conquered the island in 69 BC, but allowed Cydonia to become an independent city-state. By AD 395, the city was under Byzantine rule, which lasted until AD 824, when Arabs took over. The latter renamed the city Chania, but in AD 961, it was retaken by the Byzantine Empire. In 1204, however, the Fourth Crusade brought about the fall of Byzantium in the region, and Crete was given to Bonifacio de Montferrat, who sold it to the Venetians.

In 1252, the Venetians overcame Cretan resistance, but Chania was seized by the Genoans in 1263 and held by them until 1285. After that, all of Crete came under a settled period of Venetian rule. The spread of the Ottoman Empire put an end to that, however. In 1645, Turkey invaded the island, and within three years it had fallen under Ottoman control. In 1821, the Greeks rose against the Ottoman Empire, and many Cretans took part in the subsequent War of Independence, but the Turks enlisted the aid of Egypt, whose troops waged a bloody campaign in the island, crushing all resistance. When the Greeks were given independence in 1832, Crete was not included; instead, the island was given to the Egyptians for their help in the war. The defeat of the Egyptians by the Syrians in 1840 saw it handed back to Turkey, however. It was not until 1898, after a number of uprisings that Crete finally gained freedom from Turkish control.

The first lighthouse at Chania was established around 1570, during the period of Venetian rule. The tower that stands today, however, was largely remodeled by the Egyptians, and it sits on the base of the earlier structure. Constructed in 1864, the 85ft (26m) tall, cylindrical stone tower is on the end of the breakwater on the eastern side of the harbor entrance. Although the original lantern is no longer in operation, a red flashing light is mounted on top to guide vessels into the port.

Far left: *The original lighthouse at Chania was remodeled by the Egyptians during their occupation of the island between 1821 and 1841, and displays a distinctly Egyptian appearance in the form of its minaret-like shape. Prior to its renovation in the twenty-first century, the lighthouse appeared forlorn.*

Top right: *The major renovation program, which took place over several years, was completed in 2006. Today, the pristine tower provides a striking sight for the passengers of the many cruise ships that visit this historic Mediterranean port, and it is a popular subject for photographers.*

Right: *The setting sun casts a golden light over the hills of the island of Crete, throwing the lighthouse into stark silhouette. Soon, it will cast its own light over the sea.*

Chania, Crete, Greece

Chania Lighthouse, Chania

Sea of Crete

Souda

Rethymno

Heraklion

Libyan Sea

INVASION FORCE
When the Turks invaded Crete, they chose Chania as their beachhead. Some 60,000 troops were landed at the port from 400 ships.

Chumbe Lighthouse

Chumbe Island, Zanzibar, Tanzania

- **Chumbe Island sits in a main shipping channel between the group of islands known as Zanzibar and the mainland of Tanzania, East Africa. For over a hundred years, the lighthouse has aided the safe passage of ships through the channel.**
- **This striking lighthouse is the only one in Zanzibar that is fully maintained.**
- **The lighting equipment in use was installed in 1926 and continues to do sterling duty.**

For many people, Zanzibar is a name that conjures up exotic images of tropical islands and warm azure seas dotted with picturesque Arab dhows. Located in the Indian Ocean off the east coast of Africa and belonging to Tanzania, Zanzibar comprises two main islands, Pemba and Unguja (often known as Zanzibar), and around fifty much smaller islets. One of these is Chumbe, a chunk of coral—just over half a mile (1km) long and 984ft (300m) wide—that breaks the surface in the Zanzibar Channel, which separates the islands from the mainland. In such a busy shipping channel, a lighthouse was essential to warn shipping of Chumbe's presence.

Chumbe Lighthouse was built by the British in 1904, when the islands were a British protectorate ruled by the Sultan of Zanzibar. The five-stage, square, pyramidal tower stands 121ft (37m) high and is built from fossilized coral rock, of which there was a plentiful supply. Next to the lighthouse is a single-story keeper's cottage, while nearby there is a small mosque so that the Muslim keepers could pray. The tower is equipped with a gallery, and a lantern that contains the original Fresnel lens and the acetylene lighting system installed in 1926, although the lighthouse is no longer manned, having been automated for many years.

Although the light itself continued to be maintained, the lack of staff meant that the tower and other buildings were allowed to deteriorate. However, in the 1990s, Chumbe Island was leased by a private company, which turned it into a marine park and coral reef sanctuary. The company carried out vital restoration work on the tower and mosque, and turned the keeper's cottage into a visitor center, complete with restaurant and schoolroom for visiting parties of children. In addition, seven eco-cottages were built for tourists. Today, visitors can climb the 131 steps to the top of the lighthouse to gain breathtaking views of the islands and the surrounding ocean.

Far left: *The weathered coral walls of Chumbe Lighthouse tower above one of the seven bungalows, known as "eco-bandas," which have casuarina poles lashed together with coconut rope to form the walls, and clamshell-like roofs woven from palm fronds. Built to have minimal impact on the environment, the bandas have rainwater recycling systems, and, only a few paces along a sandy path to the beach, offer magnificent sea views.*

Top right: *Chumbe Lighthouse, set against a glorious sunset, is the dominant feature on the tiny island, and remains a vital aid to shipping navigation in the Zanzibar Channel.*

Right: *Chumbe is truly an island paradise, with waving palm trees, dense coral-rag forests, and colorful coral reefs populated by more than 400 species of fish. The eco-accommodation eschews conventional resort facilities—there are no televisions, cocktail bars, swimming pools, and no electricity—and it is ironic that the lighthouse is perhaps the most technologically advanced feature on the island.*

Chumbe Island, Zanzibar, Tanzania

Chumbe Lighthouse, Chumbe Island

Zanzibar

Bagamoyo

Dar Es Salaam

NO ALARM RAISED

On September 20, 1914, during World War I, the Chumbe Lighthouse played an unwitting role in the sinking of the Royal Navy cruiser HMS *Pegasus*. A German warship in the area, the *Königsberg*, received word that the *Pegasus* was anchored in Zanzibar harbor and sailed to attack. It is certain that the lighthouse keepers at Chumbe saw the German ship, but they failed to raise the alarm, probably through fear for their lives. As a result, the heavily outgunned British ship was destroyed with the loss of 38 lives.

Enoshima Lighthouse

Enoshima Island, Japan

• **The Enoshima Observation Tower and Lighthouse is a most remarkable looking structure that is a major feature of the Samuel Cocking Garden on Enoshima Island, just off the Japanese east coast, to the south of the capital, Tokyo.**

• **The skeletal steel tower is illuminated at night, producing a most dramatic effect.**

• **Despite its unusual appearance, the lighthouse remains an active aid to navigation.**

The small Japanese island of Enoshima—it is only about 2.5 miles (4km) in circumference—sits at the mouth of the Katase River, in Sagami Bay, and is part of the city of Fujisawa in Kanagawa Prefecture. The island is very close to the coast and is actually connected to the mainland by a 1,970ft (600m) long bridge. The island is a popular tourist destination and contains a number of attractions, including three shrines, and a cave said to be the lair of a dragon! At the top of the tiny, triangular island is the Samuel Cocking Garden, and aside from its botanical treasures, this garden is home to a futuristic observation tower and lighthouse.

Samuel Cocking was a British merchant who lived in Japan and had a Japanese wife. In 1880, Cocking purchased a plot of land at the top of Enoshima Island in his wife's name and established the Enoshima Botanical Garden. He built a 6,460sq ft (600sq m) glasshouse and amassed a collection of tropical plants. In 1923, the glasshouse was destroyed by the Great Kanto earthquake and was never rebuilt. However, the garden remained an attraction, eventually coming under control of the city of Fujisawa in 1949. By then no trace of the glasshouse could be found, but reconstruction work in 2002 uncovered its foundations, allowing the building to be reconstructed as part of a new garden. Today, the Samuel Cocking Garden attracts around half a million visitors a year.

In 1951, an observation tower supporting a nautical light was built in the Samuel Cocking Garden. Like the present tower, it was a fascinating structure with a central column and skeletal framework of triangular landings connected by open-air stairways. On top was a two-stage, octagonal observation deck surmounted by a tall mast.

In 2003, the 197ft (60m) high tower was rebuilt with a new spiral stairway, still outside, and a large-diameter, glazed observation deck. A lantern is mounted on top of the observation deck and displays a white flashing light.

Far left: *The Enoshima Observation Tower and Lighthouse is a truly dramatic looking structure. Its large, glazed observation deck is supported by an outer framework of round steel tubes connected by a series of girder "collars." The tubes lean outward, making the diameter of the tower narrower at the bottom than at the top.*

Top right: *The observation tower/lighthouse stands on the highest point of Enoshima Island and can be seen clearly from out to sea.*

Right: *At night, the tower is illuminated by floodlights that throw the framework into stark relief. The lights change color to a regular rythmn, adding to the intriguing spectacle.*

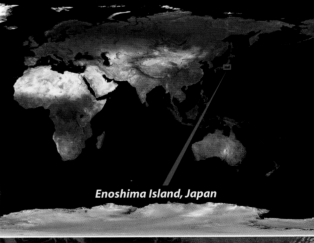

Enoshima Island, Japan

Enoshima Lighthouse, Enoshima Island

• Tokyo

• Nirasaki

• Yokohama

Fuji •

• Hamamatsu

VERTIGINOUS CLIMB

The Enoshima Observation Tower and Lighthouse provides stunning, panoramic views of Sagami Bay and famous Mount Fuji. However, the climb up the outside of the central column is not for the faint-hearted or those who suffer from vertigo!

Fanad Head Lighthouse

County Donegal, Ireland

- **The Fanad Head Lighthouse stands on a rugged headland that thrusts out into the Atlantic Ocean from Ireland's northwest coast.**

- **Built in the late nineteenth century, the lighthouse remains in use today and not only marks a dangerous area for shipping, but also the entrance to Lough Swilly, a natural harbor of refuge.**

- **The current lighthouse is the second to be built on the spot, the first dating from the early nineteenth century.**

The west coast of Ireland is a dramatic and beautiful landscape, much of it jagged and rocky, but it is exposed to the full force of Atlantic storms and is a perilous region for shipping. For this reason, a major lighthouse building program was carried out during the nineteenth century, and many of those lighthouses remain in operation, continuing to protect the lives of seafarers in these dangerous waters. In the northwest, in the county of Donegal, lies a long, narrow inlet known as Lough Swilly, a natural harbor bordered in the west by Fanad Head.

The first lighthouse at Fanad Head was built directly as a result of a shipwreck. In 1812, a Royal Navy frigate, the *Saldana*, foundered on the headland with the loss of the entire crew. Shortly after, a local naval officer suggested that a lighthouse be built on the headland, stating that had one existed, the *Saldana* would not have been lost. In those days, all of Ireland was under the administration of the British, and Irish lighthouses were the responsibility of Trinity House. They agreed with the officer and made plans to build a lighthouse there.

A three-story, narrow stone tower was erected and equipped with a fixed catoptric light showing red to seaward and white toward the lough. The light comprised nine oil lamps with parabolic reflectors, and was first lit on March 17, 1817.

By the early 1870s, it was realized that improvements were needed to the light at Fanad Head, and several options were considered, but it was not until the 1880s that any work was undertaken. A new, larger tower was built, standing 72ft (22m) high and linked to a two-story keeper's house by a covered walkway.

Far left: *A lighthouse has stood atop the steep cliffs of Fanad Head since 1817, marking the treacherous headland and the position of the Limeburner Rock offshore, an isolated rock that lies just below the surface, waiting to tear into any vessels that come too near. The current lighthouse, and an additional dwelling were built in the 1880s.*

Top right: *The lighthouse began operation on September 1, 1886. It was equipped originally with kerosene oil lamps, but these were changed to an incandescent kerosene burner in 1906. In 1975, an electric light was installed. This flashes white with red sectors over Limeburner Rock and the nearby Swilly Rocks.*

Right: *Fanad Head Lighthouse is well served by its white-painted keepers' houses and their ancillary buildings, making the site a permanently manned complex dedicated to saving lives at sea in the difficult waters of the Atlantic.*

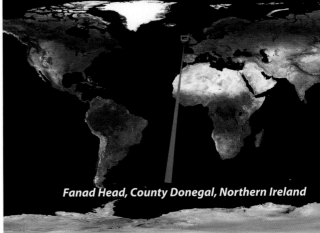

Fanad Head, County Donegal, Northern Ireland

Fanad Head Lighthouse, County Donegal

Portsalon •

• Londonderry

Donegal •

Belfast •

Sligo •

FLIGHT TO SAFETY
There was one survivor from the wreck of the *Saldana* on Fanad Head, the ship's parrot. The bird had managed to escape and fly to safety, being identified by a silver collar inscribed with the ship's name.

Cape Neddick Lighthouse

York, Maine, USA

• **Cape Neddick Lighthouse stands on a rocky islet called the Nubble, just off Cape Neddick Point, about 2 miles (3.2km) north of the entrance to York River and York Harbor on the coast of Maine.**

• **Built in the late nineteenth century, the 41ft (12.5m) high cylindrical tower remains in operation.**

• **Because of its location, the lighthouse is usually referred to as the Nubble Light, or quite simply the Nubble.**

The town of York, in Maine, was a prosperous port during the early nineteenth century, but vessels heading from the north of Cape Neddick Point to the town's harbor had to make their way around the treacherous rocky outcrop of the Nubble. Local seafarers knew of the danger and, as early as 1807, urged that a lighthouse be built on the islet, but their pleas were ignored. A subsequent proposal to construct a lighthouse in 1837 was turned down by the Lighthouse Service because it considered there were enough other lights in the vicinity. Despite these lights, vessels continued to be lost, among them the bark *Isidore*, which foundered near Bald Head Cliff, just north of the Nubble, in 1842. It is said that this ship regularly appears as a ghost ship, complete with a phantom crew.

Eventually, in 1876, Congress appropriated funds for the construction of a lighthouse on the Nubble. Built from cast-iron sections lined with brick, the tower was equipped with a fixed red light. Because of the height of the island, the light was actually 88ft (27m) above sea level. Alongside the lighthouse was a fog bell with an automatic striking mechanism. This was suspended within a skeletal tower. Subsequently, this was replaced by a wooden pyramidal tower in 1911. In 1961, the bell was replaced by a diaphragm horn.

The lighthouse was fully automated on July 13, 1987. Despite this, the lantern room remains largely original, retaining most of its brass fittings, although a plastic lens has replaced the previous glass item.

Far left: *Cape Neddick Lighthouse and the adjacent two-story keeper's house were completed in 1879, and the light was illuminated for the first time on July 1 of that year. An unusual aspect of the gallery around the lantern is that the stanchions are topped by small brass replicas of the lighthouse, a rare decorative feature on such a utilitarian building.*

Top right: *As night approaches and the lighthouse is picked out by the glow of the setting sun, the lantern shines out as a warning to vessels to keep clear of the rocky Nubble.*

Right: *The well-kept lighthouse and keeper's house provide a picturesque contrast to the rugged islet on which they stand.*

York, Maine, USA

Concord •

Manchester •

Boston •

Cape Neddick Lighthouse, York

• Springfield

Providence •

BUCKET SEAT

In 1602, the English explorer and privateer Bartholomew Gosnold named the Nubble "Savage Rock" after encountering a group of hostile Indians there.

For many years, the Cape Neddick Lighthouse keepers used a large, box-shaped bucket suspended from a cable to obtain supplies from the mainland. In the late 1960s, one keeper used to put his two children in the bucket to send them off to school, but when this came to the attention of the local district commander, arrangements were made for them to board on the mainland, and no further families with school-age children were sent to the Nubble.

Cape Trafalgar Lighthouse

Cádiz Province, Spain

• **Located on a sandy promontory that juts out into the Atlantic Ocean near the southern tip of Spain, Cape Trafalgar Lighthouse overlooks the northwestern entrance to the Strait of Gibraltar.**

• **The lighthouse was constructed during the mid-nineteenth century and has an unusual "fluted" appearance thanks to strengthening ribs that were added to support a larger lantern.**

• **Unusually, in these days of automation, the lighthouse continues to be manned.**

A relatively unassuming headland on the Spanish Atlantic coast, Cape Trafalgar is famous throughout the world for the naval battle that took place a few miles offshore on October 21, 1805, between a British fleet commanded by Admiral Horatio Nelson, and a combined French and Spanish fleet. The British gained a memorable victory, but Nelson was mortally wounded during the fighting. At that time, there was no lighthouse on the cape, and the nearby beaches were known locally as the "calderas" (boiling pots) because of the large number of ships that were wrecked there.

The lighthouse was not built until 1862, a 112ft (34m) high, round, stone tower being erected at the very tip of the headland. Attached to the bottom of the tower was a single-story keeper's dwelling. In 1926, the lantern was replaced by a larger structure, which required the slim tower to be reinforced by the addition of a number of strengthening ribs. Unusually, there are two galleries, one around the lantern and the other around the watchroom below it.

Far left: *Standing alone on a windswept, sandy headland, the stark, white-painted Cape Trafalgar Lighthouse makes a dramatic statement against the deep blue of the sky. For over 140 years, the tower has marked the cape and the Alcetera Bank, which lies offshore to the north.*

Top right: *Before a new, larger lantern could be installed during the 1920s, it was necessary to strengthen the tower by the addition of eight vertical ribs. These meet in a ring of reinforcement just below the watchroom.*

Right: *Today, the lighthouse makes a fascinating landmark for the sunbathers and picnickers who throng the nearby beaches in summer.*

Cádiz Province, Spain

Cape Trafalgar Lighthouse, Cádiz Province

• Huelva

Cádiz •

Marbella •

• Gibraltar

Tangier •

MYSTERY OF THE FIXED LIGHT

On the night of March 30, 1881, the British steamship *Jeanie* was wrecked about 2½ miles (4km) to the north of the Cape Trafalgar Lighthouse. The vessel ran aground on the Alcetera Bank and became stranded, eventually breaking up in the heavy surf. All but one of the crew managed to get ashore safely, but nothing of the cargo could be salvaged. It transpired that the crew of the ship had mistaken the Cape Trafalgar light for another farther to the south. This was because the light appeared as a fixed light rather than the correct revolving light. All of the crew swore that this was the case and that the light remained fixed until extinguished the following morning; a British court of inquiry found no reason to doubt them. The reason for the lighthouse showing a fixed light rather than a revolving one was never ascertained.

Guia Lighthouse

Macau, China

• **Guia Lighthouse, also known as Fortaleza da Guia Light, was the first Western-style lighthouse to be built on the Chinese coast, and today it is the oldest surviving lighthouse in the country.**

• **Part of the Guia Fortress complex, a UNESCO World Heritage site, the nineteenth-century lighthouse not only remains an active aid to navigation, but also is a tourist attraction.**

• **Standing on a hill in the center of the city of Macau, the lighthouse can be seen from a distance of 16 miles (26km) out to sea.**

The Chinese Special Administrative Region of Macau is a former Portuguese colony. In fact, it was the oldest and last European colony in China, being handed back to the Chinese at the end of 1999. It lies to the west of the Pearl River delta, facing the South China Sea to the south and east. Portuguese traders established a settlement and port on the Macau Peninsula in the middle of the sixteenth century, but as the port prospered so it became a target for other seafaring colonial powers, most notably the Dutch, who made several attempts to seize it during the seventeenth century.

To meet the threat from the Dutch, the residents of Macau built a fortress on top of Guia Hill, the highest hill on the peninsula. It is known that there was some form of fortification on the site as early as 1622, but the present fort was not completed until March of 1638. This fortress had sentry posts, magazines, and watchtowers; in fact, it remained a restricted military zone until 1976. The fortress covers an area of around 8,600sq ft (800sq m) and has 20ft (6m) high walls with crenellations for cannons.

In 1864, construction began of Guia Lighthouse within the walls of the fortress, being completed in the following year. The 49ft (15m) high round stone tower is 46ft (14m) across at the bottom and tapers to 33ft (10m) at the top, where there is a gallery and lantern. Originally, the kerosene light was mounted on a wooden wheel and was rotated by means of a rope system.

In 1874, a typhoon severely damaged the lighthouse, such that it remained out of action for the following thirty years. It was not illuminated again until 1910 after extensive repairs and the installation of more modern lighting with mirrored reflectors.

Far left: *The lighthouse was built alongside Guia Chapel, which was constructed prior to 1622. The exterior appearance of the tower was deliberately understated, and bears decorative features around the windows and doorway, and sensitive coloring that would not detract from the graceful architecture of the chapel.*

Top right: *The walls of the tower have a plain, smooth rendered finish, while the window openings are surrounded by exposed stonework lintels. The purely decorative canopies over the rectangular windows feature ornate molded corbels.*

Right: *The lighthouse and the chapel make a perfect partnership—in their own way both are guiding lights.*

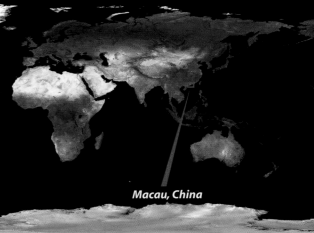

Macau, China

Guia Lighthouse, Macau

SEEING THE LIGHT

On April 16, 2008, the government of Macau issued a regulation to ensure that Guia Lighthouse would continue to be visible from the sea. Local development plans for highrise buildings threatened to obscure the historic tower—in fact, the construction of some buildings had already been approved and started. However, public pressure, UN pressure on the Chinese government, and pressure by the Chinese on the Macau administration led to a height restriction being placed on all buildings that would affect the lighthouse's sight lines.

Head Harbour Lighthouse

Campobello Island, Canada

- **The historic Head Harbour Lighthouse, built in the early nineteenth century, continues to play a major role in guiding shipping around Canada's rocky Campobello Island in Passamaquoddy Bay.**

- **The lighthouse is one of the oldest surviving wooden towers in Canada and was the second lighthouse to be built in the area after the West Quoddy Head Light across the international border in Maine.**

- **The lighthouse is also known locally as the East Quoddy Head Light.**

Campobello Island is the largest of a group of islands that lie in Passamaquoddy Bay in the Canadian province of New Brunswick, close to the border with Maine. In fact, the island is closer to the coast of the U.S. state than that of New Brunswick. As a child, former U.S. President Franklin D. Roosevelt spent his summers on Campobello Island, where his family had a second home. It was there that he contracted polio.

The sea around the island is peppered with shoals and jagged rocks that lie just below the surface, and there is a high tidal range. Making things worse for seafarers are the frequent fogs that roll in from the Bay of Fundy farther out to sea.

The early nineteenth century saw a burgeoning of trade between Campobello Island and the coast of Maine 7.5 miles (12km) away. Although much of it was legitimate, the American town of Eastport, opposite the island, was a center for smugglers, and many illicit goods found their way across the border via Campobello. With such a high level of marine activity, it was essential that the hazards in Passamaquoddy Bay and around the island were marked, leading to the construction of the first lighthouse in 1808, the American West Quoddy Head Light, which was level with the southern tip of Campobello Island.

In 1829, the Head Harbour Lighthouse was established on the rocky northern tip of the island. The 51ft (15.5m) high, octagonal wooden tower is pyramidal and clad with shingles. A flared cornice supports the gallery and lantern. The current cast-iron lantern replaced the original in 1887. The building is painted white with a large red cross emblazoned on its side. Subsequently, a keeper's house was added, along with a boathouse and fog horn building.

Far left: *The white painted shingle cladding, emblazoned with a red cross on all elevations, is a highly visible daymark for shipping. Decorative touches were added in the form of the cornice supporting the lantern base, and the shaped hoods over the windows.*

Top right: *The fog alarm building stands adjacent to the lighthouse, with the dwelling between. The tower is attached to the dwelling by a covered walkway, and is also accessible from outside by a door on the southwest side*

Right: *The lighthouse sits on a rocky outcropping that becomes an islet at high tide, at the northernmost point of Campobello Island. It can be reached on foot for only two hours when the tide is out, by an arduous route down slippery metal ladders, crossing two islets connected by a wooden bridge, and a walk across a seaweed covered intertidal zone. The crossing can be dangerous, and even lighthouse keepers have lost their lives by misjudging the frigid, fast rising tidal currents.*

Campobello Island, Canada

CANADA

• St. John

USA

Bay of Fundy

Grand Manan Island

Nova Scotia

Head Harbour Lighthouse, Campobello Island

CROSS OF ST. GEORGE

The red cross painted on the side of the Head Harbour Lighthouse represents the Cross of St. George, the national flag of England. It is not known when it was first painted on the lighthouse, but it goes back at least as far as the Canadian Confederation, when the Dominion of Canada was formed from the provinces and territories of British North America. It was not merely an act of nationalism, however, since the cross acts as an effective daymark, making positive identification of the building possible from a distance.

Hook Head Lighthouse

Waterford, Ireland

- **The lighthouse at Hook Head, on the south coast of Ireland, is one of the oldest operating lighthouses in the world, having been built originally during the twelfth century.**
- **The lighthouse stands on the site of an earlier beacon fire that was established by Augustine monks during the fifth century.**
- **At some unrecorded point in its history, the lighthouse was made larger by the simple expedient of constructing an outer wall around the existing tower and inserting a stairway between the two walls.**

On the south coast of Ireland, three rivers—the Nore, Suir, and Barrow, known as the Three Sisters—come together to form a single, narrow estuary and natural deepwater harbor, at the head of which is the city of Waterford. The harbor is enclosed by two headlands: Craden in the west and Hook in the east. It is on the latter that the Hook Head Lighthouse has stood for around 800 years, but the history of the nautical light in this location goes back much farther.

In the fifth century, a Welsh monk by the name of Dubhán founded a monastery near Hook Head and soon established a beacon fire on the headland for the benefit of local seafarers. The monks of the monastery continued to maintain the beacon for several hundred years until the arrival of a Norman nobleman called Raymond LeGros around 1170. Within a couple of years, he had built a fortified stone tower, the Tower of Hook, on the headland to replace the beacon and guard the harbor entrance. Despite its warlike overtones, the tower was left in the custody of the monks once more.

The monks continued to tend the beacon, even through the suppressions of the monasteries that occurred during the reign of Henry VIII. In 1641, however, with the outbreak of the English Civil War, the monks left the monastery for good. No one else took responsibility for the beacon, which was extinguished, leading to many shipwrecks. It was not until 1667, after Charles II had authorized Sir Richard Reading to build six lighthouses around the coast of Ireland, that the beacon on top of the Tower of Hook was reestablished.

The beacon fires continued in use until the 1790s, when a lantern incorporating oil lamps and reflectors was installed. The present lantern and Fresnel lens were fitted in 1864, and over the years, the light has been fueled by oil, coal gas, kerosene, and finally electricity. Today, the light is fully automated.

Far left: *Built from local limestone on a rugged and dangerous peninsula, Hook Head Lighthouse has guided mariners for over 800 years. The original twelfth-century tower was 59ft (18m) high and around 28ft (8.5m) in diameter, but when enlarged with the new outer wall in the seventeenth century, it grew to a height of 79ft (24m) and a diameter of around 39ft (12m).*

Top right: *After the lighthouse was automated in 1996, it was opened to the public. Today, visitors can climb the 115 steps to the top of the first stage, where a walkway provides splendid views of the surrounding countryside and the ocean. Inside the lighthouse, there are displays that chart the history of the ancient structure.*

Right: *The façade of the tower belies the earlier structure that lies within. The latter was based on the freestanding, cylindrical keeps, known as "Juliets," that were popular with the Normans during the twelfth century.*

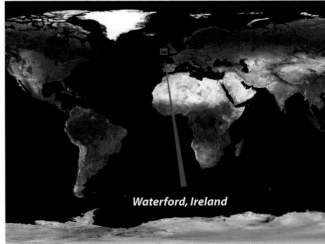

Waterford, Ireland

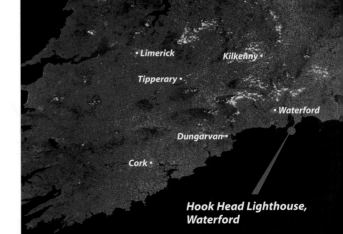

- Limerick
- Kilkenny
- Tipperary
- Waterford
- Dungarvan
- Cork

Hook Head Lighthouse, Waterford

LOST IN TRANSLATION

Hook Head was named originally Rinn Dubhán, or Dubhán Point, after the monk who first lit the beacon there. Coincidentally, "dubhán" means "hook" in the Irish language, so eventually the headland became known as Hook Point and then Hook Head.

La Lanterna

Genoa, Italy

- La Lanterna is a tall, imposing tower that looks out over the historic port city of Genoa on the Gulf of Liguria in northwest Italy.
- Built in the mid-sixteenth century, the lighthouse has withstood bombardment from the sea and remains an operational aid to navigation.
- The tallest brick lighthouse in the world, it is a popular landmark and recognized symbol of the city, proudly bearing its coat of arms.

The history of the port of Genoa goes back to ancient times. Its first inhabitants were Ligurians, and there is evidence that it was occupied by Greeks during the sixth and fifth centuries BC, although it is thought that the harbor may have been used by the Etruscans and Phoenicians before that. Long a city of seafarers, it was the birthplace of Christopher Columbus, whose uncle, Antonio, became the keeper of the previous lighthouse that stood on the site of La Lanterna in 1449. Today, Genoa remains an important port, and the lighthouse of La Lanterna is its leading aid to navigation, guiding shipping safely into the harbor.

It is thought that the earlier lighthouse, which was almost as tall as La Lanterna, was erected on the site in 1128. The foundations of this tower were damaged during the war between the Guelphs and Ghibellines in 1318, which led to subsequent reinforcement and the construction of a moat around it. War caused further damage in 1506, when the upper part was partially destroyed—by mistake—by Genoese insurgents fighting the French. It was not until 1543, however, that the tower was rebuilt in its present form.

Standing 253ft (77m) high, La Lanterna is a magnificent, two-stage, square tower with a gallery at the top of each stage and a lantern on the very top. The latter is constructed from wood sheathed in copper and lead. This had to be replaced in 1864 after the French bombarded the city from the sea and scored a hit on the lantern. In 1936, the lighting system was electrified, producing a light of 750,000 candlepower. It is visible from 29 miles (46km) out to sea.

Far left: *La Lanterna is one of the oldest standing structures of its kind anywhere in the world. Its two square sections, which are almost the same height, each have a projecting gallery. Visitors are welcomed to the lighthouse, where they can climb the 172 steps to the first gallery to gain breathtaking views over the surrounding city.*

Top right: *Built on a rock 132ft (40m) high, the top of La Lanterna is 384ft (117m) above sea level, and its light can be seen from more than 31 miles (50km) away.*

Right: *The lighthouse projects above the quay, crowded with huge liners at dock. The area surrounding the lighthouse was restored to include the Museo della Lanterna, a museum covering the history of the port and the navigational aids used at sea, including an example of a Fresnel lens similar to that used in La Lanterna.*

Genoa, Italy

La Lanterna, Genoa

OLIVE OIL FUEL

The tower that stood on the site of La Lanterna Lighthouse had a beacon fire originally fueled by heather and gorse. In 1326, the first lamp was installed, using olive oil for fuel. This oil was still being employed in La Lanterna in 1840, when the first rotating light system was fitted, along with a Fresnel lens. It was not until 1913 that an oil-vapor lamp was fitted. With the 72in (1840mm) diameter optics, this generated a 520,000-candlepower beam. The rotation was controlled by a clockwork mechanism that had to be wound every five hours.

Ile Louët Lighthouse

Morlaix, France

- **Clinging to the side of a bare, rocky outcrop in the Bay of Morlaix, on the northwest coast of France, Ile Louët Lighthouse marks the entrance to Morlaix Roads.**
- **Dating from the late nineteenth century, the lighthouse is one of several built on islands in the bay, helping vessels to thread their way through the difficult waters.**
- **The current lighthouse replaced a previous day beacon, which had been in use since 1794.**

Far left: *Ile Louët, with its elegant lighthouse and quaint keeper's cottage, is one of several small picturesque islands in the Bay of Morlaix. Adjacent to the rocky islet is another, low lying islet, on which sits Le Châteaux de Taureau, a 16th century fortress designed to protect the town from attack by the English, now a popular tourist attraction.*

The Bay of Morlaix is named after the French town of Morlaix, which is 25 miles (40km) east of Brest in the Brittany region of northwest France. Morlaix falls under the administrative department of Finistère, the name having been derived from the Latin "Finis Terrae," meaning "end of the earth." This is comparable to Land's End in England on the opposite side of the English Channel, since Finistère refers to the most westerly part of metropolitan France, which juts out into the Channel where it joins the Atlantic. This part of the French coast is noted for its rugged and rocky landscape, where many of the inlets, known as abers, are distinctly fjord-like in appearance.

Morlaix, built on the slopes of a steep valley, has long been an important port in the region, and its bay contains a number of small islands, making passage in and out of its harbor a task that requires great care. Several of the islands have lighthouses for this very reason, while others are home to an imposing sixteenth-century château, and a few more modest private cottages.

The lighthouse on the Ile Louët, which is on the west side of the entrance to Morlaix Roads, was built in 1860 and has a 39ft (12m) high, square stone tower, on top of which is a gallery and lantern. The lighthouse was manned until 1962, when it was automated. It plays an important role as the front light for the main channel that enters the Bay of Morlaix, the nearby Lande Light acting as the rear light.

Top right: *Attached to the side of the lighthouse tower is a single-story cottage, built originally for the keeper, although a less utilitarian dormer windowed cottage was constructed nearby in 1910.*

Right: *The light flashes three times every twelve seconds, and shows green or white, depending on the direction from which it is seen.*

Bay of Morlaix, France

Ile Louët Lighthouse, Bay of Morlaix

- *Morlaix*
- *Brest*
- *Saint-Malo*
- *Quimper*
- *Rennes*
- *Vannes*

PIRATE STRONGHOLD

Morlaix is one of the great Breton ports, and during the "Golden Period" of the late Middle Ages, it enjoyed a thriving trade with England, just across the Channel. However, the town also has a darker side, since it became the home of a group of pirates, enjoying even greater notoriety than a hotbed of piracy farther east along the coast, St. Malo.

When the five-year-old Mary Queen of Scots passed through Morlaix in 1548, such was the clamor to see her that the town's gates were wrenched from their hinges and all the chains from the bridges were broken.

Pâquis Lighthouse

Geneva, Switzerland

- **The Pâquis Lighthouse is unusual because it marks the harbor of the Swiss city of Geneva on the vast, landlocked Lake Geneva.**

- **The ornate tower, also known as the Gèneve Light, was built during the late nineteenth century and stands on the site of an earlier, experimental light.**

- **The lighthouse is a popular landmark of the city and a tourist attraction, being floodlit at night.**

Lake Geneva, or Lake Léman as it is also known, is a huge, crescent-shaped lake that was carved out between the Swiss mountains thousands of years ago by a withdrawing glacier. It is the second largest freshwater lake in Central Europe, being 45 miles (73km) long and 8.7 miles (14km) wide. The lake is fed by the Rhône, Venoge, Dranse, and Aubonne rivers, and it comes under the jurisdiction of two countries, Switzerland and France. Toward the western end, the lake narrows considerably, the narrow portion being referred to as the Petit Lac (Small Lake) and the remainder as the Grand Lac (Large Lake).

The lake is so large that for centuries it was used as a transport artery with a substantial amount of commercial shipping plying back and forth. That is no longer the case, but it is still used by passenger ferries and lots of pleasure craft.

At the western end of the lake, at the exit point of the Rhone River, is Geneva, the second largest city in Switzerland and the largest in the French-speaking region of the country. Geneva is considered by many to be an "international" city because of the presence of many international organizations, among them many United Nations agencies, not to mention the Red Cross. The city is said to offer the second highest quality of life in the world, and contributing to that is the bustling waterfront along the shore of the lake and the availability of many different types of watersport. Boats are a way of life for many residents.

Pâquis Lighthouse has marked the harbor at Geneva since 1896, standing on the end of the dock known as the Jetée des Pâquis. The 56ft (17m) high, octagonal tower was built from cast iron on a stone base and is painted completely white. Its fixed light shows white or green depending on the direction from which it is viewed.

Far left: *As an alpine country, Switzerland seems a most unlikely location for a lighthouse, but it has several on two large lakes. These have more than just a decorative function, since there is navigation on both stretches of water. The most well known is the Pâquis Lighthouse, known as the Feu des Pâquis, which marks the end of Geneva's Jetée des Pâquis on Lac Léman (Lake Geneva).*

Top right: *Silhouetted against a clear blue sky with rugged mountains and lush lakeside foliage in the background, the lighthouse displays its ornate, cast-iron structure, which is a popular subject for photographers and vacationers.*

Right: *At night, floodlights pick out the intricacies of the structure in a counterplay of light and shadow.*

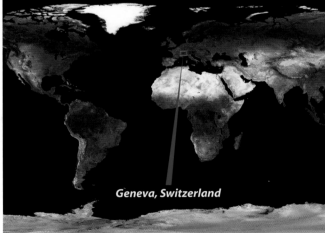

Geneva, Switzerland

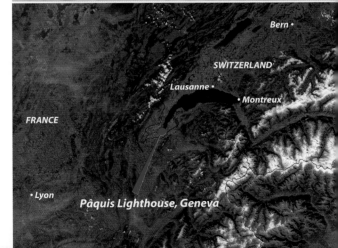

Pâquis Lighthouse, Geneva

ARC LIGHT

The first lighthouse to be erected on the Jetée des Pâquis, 1857, was constructed to test an early form of electric lighting, whereby the light was actually provided by an open electric arc. Unfortunately, the results were not very encouraging and the experiment was abandoned.

Sullivan's Island Lighthouse

Charleston, USA

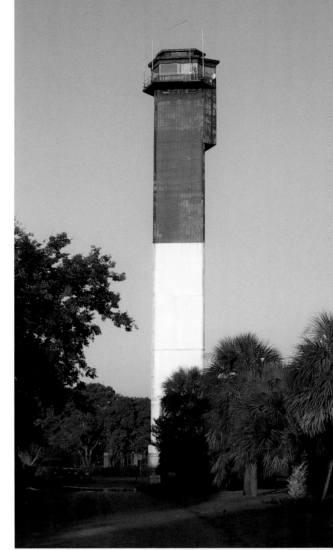

Far left: *An unconventional form for a lighthouse, Sullivan's Island Lighthouse is a monolithic structure with a triangular section, pointing seaward, which can withstand winds of up to 125mph (201km/h). Although air conditioning makes life tolerable inside the lighthouse for the keepers, and an elevator whisks them up the tower in just 74 seconds, it is still necessary to scale a 25-ft (7.6m) ladder to the lantern room.*

- **The unusual-looking lighthouse at Sullivan's Island marks the entrance to Charleston Harbor on the Atlantic coast of South Carolina. It is also known as the Charleston Light and the New Charleston Light.**
- **The trapezoidal tower was the last lighthouse to be built by the United States Coast Guard, having been constructed during the 1960s.**
- **The tower is the only lighthouse in the United States to have an elevator and air conditioning.**

Located on the East Coast of the United States, the State of South Carolina has a relatively short coastline bordering the North Atlantic Ocean. The state's main seaport is Charleston, which has a long history going back to the early colonial days. By the middle of the eighteenth century, it was the major center of Atlantic trade for the southern colonies, and the largest and richest city south of Philadelphia. By 1770, it had become the fourth largest port in the colonies. There was a flourishing trade in the export of rice and indigo, grown locally on slave-owning plantations, which led to a very profitable shipping industry. In those days, Charleston was the cultural and economic center of the South. Today, it is the second largest container port on the East Coast and the second most productive port in the world after Hong Kong.

Sullivan's Island is on the north side of the entrance to Charleston Harbor and was chosen as the site for a new, 163ft (50m) high lighthouse when coastal erosion threatened the existing harbor light at Morris Island on the south side of the entrance. The current tower is not the first lighthouse to have stood on the island, however, since a much smaller tower was erected on the southern end of the island in 1848, while an extra light was added in 1872 to create a pair of range lights.

The present lighthouse was commissioned in 1962. Built from concrete and steel with aluminum siding, it has an overhanging lantern. Originally, it was equipped with a 28-million-candlepower light, although subsequently this was removed in favor of two less-powerful aerobeacons. Even so, the light can still be seen from 26 miles (42km) out to sea.

Top right: *The original lantern boasted a 28-million-candlepower light, but this was considered dangerous and bothersome to those living nearby, and it was downgraded to a light of just one million candlepower. Originally the lighthouse was painted red, but the color was so unpopular with locals that it was changed to its current black top, white bottom scheme.*

Right: *The light comprises two DCB-24 beacons, which flash every second. The two lights are mounted at different angles, and rotate at about 2rpm. The lantern room—here shown in side view—looks more like an air traffic control tower and has a six-sided gallery.*

Sullivan's Island, Charleston, USA

Orangeburg •

Georgetown •

Summerville •

Charleston •

Sullivan's Island Lighthouse, Charleston

• Savannah

HISTORIC LOCATION

Close to Sullivan's Island stands Fort Moultrie, from which Confederate soldiers opened fire on Federal forces at Fort Sumter just off the coast in 1860, the opening shots in the American Civil War.

As lighthouses go, the Sullivan's Island Lighthouse is relatively young. Even so, the U.S. Coast Guard has declared the structure surplus to requirements. It seems likely that it will be taken over by the National Park Service, which already owns the adjacent Life Saving Station, as part of the Fort Sumter National Monument. If this does occur, the Coast Guard will continue to maintain and operate the light, while the Park Service will look after the tower.

Sur Lighthouse

Sur, Oman

- **The lighthouse that marks the entrance to the Omani port of Sur demonstrates that functional buildings can also be attractive architecturally. The three-stage tower, with its arched doorway and windows, reflects the traditional Arabian architecture of the region.**
- **The lighthouse is also known as the Ras Ayqah Lighthouse after the promontory on which it stands.**
- **The flashing white light can be seen from a distance of 11.5 miles (18.5km).**

The Sultanate of Oman lies on the southeast coast of the Arabian Peninsula. To the northeast is the Gulf of Oman, which leads to the Strait of Hormuz and the Persian Gulf, and to the south and east is the Arabian Sea. The lengthy coastline has made maritime commerce an important part of the country's economy. For centuries, its waters have been plied by traditional Arab sailing vessels known as dhows, and the region has strong trading links with East Africa and India.

Near the northeast tip of the country is the city and port of Sur, which looks out onto the Gulf of Oman. It is the capital of the Ash Sharqiyah region and has long been a major dhow building city. Sur's location made it ideal as a trade center, and as early as the sixth century, it had links with East Africa. The Portuguese took control of the port in the sixteenth century, but they were driven out by Arab forces led by Nasir ibn Murshid. For many years, Sur was involved in the slave trade, until it was outlawed by the British in the mid-nineteenth century; its fortunes took a further downturn when the Suez Canal was opened, which led to a loss of trade with India.

Although the Sur Lighthouse looks as though it is quite old, in fact it is a modern structure, built during the late twentieth century. It does not really look like a lighthouse because it does not have the normal type of lantern on top. Instead, the top story of the 36ft (11m) high tower has large, arched windows through which the light is displayed. The rendered stone structure has the sandy brown color of many local buildings, which is set off by the blue domed top. The lighthouse stands on a promontory on the eastern side of the entrance to the city's harbor.

Far left: *After the repressive regime of the previous sultan was ended, Oman was allowed to develop, and many building programs were initiated. One of these included the improvement of the port facilities at Sur, and the construction of the graceful lighthouse at the entrance to the port.*

Top right: *The lighthouse commands a view over the harbor, and across to a number of forts located on the hillsides. The lighthouse and the crenellated wall that surrounds it incorporate motifs that occur in the local architecture, so that this modern building appears to be much older than it is.*

Right: *Picturesque and a practical aid to navigation in the harbor, Sur Lighthouse has become a popular tourist attraction in its own right.*

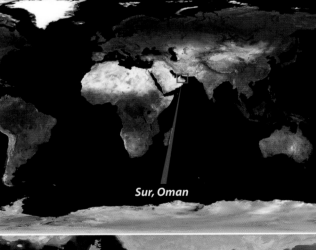

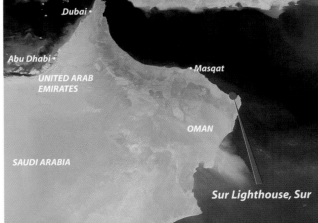

Sur, Oman

Dubai

Abu Dhabi

UNITED ARAB EMIRATES

Masqat

OMAN

SAUDI ARABIA

Sur Lighthouse, Sur

PORT MODERNIZATION

Although an independent nation since the mid-eighteenth century, for most of the twentieth century, Oman was a British military protectorate. The sultan's rule was repressive, however, and he eschewed modern developments. These included the erection of lighthouses and the development of port facilities. Eventually, in 1970, he was overthrown by his son, the present sultan, who undertook a program of modernization throughout the country, which has rapidly caught up with the remainder of the Arab world.

Swakopmund Lighthouse

Swakopmund, Namibia

- **A relic of colonial times, the Swakopmund Lighthouse stands behind the beach and marks what was once the major port of German South West Africa (now Namibia).**
- **The round stone tower, built at the beginning of the twentieth century, is one of three traditional lighthouses in Namibia that look out over the South Atlantic Ocean, ensuring that shipping keeps clears of the ominously named Skeleton Coast.**
- **The lighthouse has a 57,800-candlepower light that can be seen from 21 miles (33km) out to sea.**

Swakopmund is a relatively young city, having been founded by German settlers on the west coast of Africa in 1892. It stands at the mouth of the Swakop River, the site having been chosen because in the late nineteenth century, increasing traffic between Germany and its western African colony led to a need for the colony's own port, since the nearest existing harbor, Walvis Bay, was 21 miles (33km) to the south and in the hands of the British. Although not a natural harbor, it was the most suitable place the colonists could find.

The first settlers arrived by sea and, initially, had to create dugouts on the beach to protect themselves from severe weather. Once they had become established, prefabricated wooden houses were shipped in, since there were no local building materials. At the time, ships had to be unloaded into special boats that could be beached, but in 1898 a breakwater was constructed to create a harbor, making unloading much more efficient. Before long, Swakopmund became the main port for the entire territory.

In 1915, following the outbreak of World War I, the German colony was occupied by South African troops, and the region was administered by South Africa for the following seventy-five years. It became independent, as Namibia, in 1990.

A major landmark of Swakopmund, the lighthouse was established in 1903 as a 36ft (11m) high, round stone tower. By 1910, however, due to the continued growth of the city, it had become surrounded by buildings, which partially obscured the light. Consequently, it was rebuilt and made much taller. In 1924, the lighthouse was equipped with an acetylene gas lighting system, which was replaced by electric lighting in 1980. In 1982, a new lantern was installed with a flashing light and stainless-steel weather vane.

Far left: *In the early twentieth century, the Swakopmund Lighthouse was made much taller by building a new section on top of the original stone tower. This increased the height to 115ft (35m). The new section was rendered and painted with red and white bands to make it stand out against the backdrop of the city.*

Top right: *Unusually, the rebuilt lighthouse was given two galleries, one around the lantern and the other just below it, around the watchroom.*

Right: *Standing out starkly against the deep blue of the sky, the lighthouse is a well-known landmark in the city, which today is a major beach resort. The original part of the lighthouse can be seen as exposed stonework, while the newer, upper section is painted for high visibility.*

Swakopmund, Namibia

Swakopmund Lighthouse, Swakopumund

Windhoek •

Walvisbaai •

Solitaire •

OMINOUS COAST

The Skeleton Coast was given its name because of the large number of whale and seal bones that littered the shore during the heyday of the whaling industry, plus the many wrecks of ships that had foundered against the rocks offshore during the thick fogs that are common in the region. Over a thousand ships are known to have come to grief in these waters.

Tower of Hercules

La Coruña, Spain

- **The oldest working lighthouse in the world, the Tower of Hercules stands on the northwest tip of Spain, looking out over the Atlantic Ocean.**

- **The lighthouse is thought to have been built in the second century by the Romans, although substantial reconstruction during the late eighteenth century saw its height increased and a neoclassical façade added.**

- **Today, while continuing to act as an aid to navigation, it is also one of the most visited tourist attractions in the Spanish region of Galicia.**

Standing on a high, rocky headland close to the city of La Coruña, and almost surrounded by the crashing waves of the Atlantic, the Tower of Hercules was built by the Romans as a navigation beacon for vessels plying the rugged coast. Although the exact date of its construction is not known, an inscription on the base mentions a Roman engineer by the name of Gaius Sevius Lupus, who was known to have been active in Spain during the reign of the Emperor Trajan (AD 98–117).

The original lighthouse was a three-story stone structure that stood 112ft (34m) high, making it one of the tallest buildings ever built in Spain by the Romans, who are noted for their engineering skill. Around the outside of the building there was a wooden spiral ramp that provided access to the top, allowing fuel to be carried up to maintain the beacon fire. Today, the original 5ft (1.5m) thick walls of the structure can be seen from the inside, having been preserved by the later addition of a 2ft (60cm) thick neoclassical façade.

After the fall of Rome, the lighthouse fell into disuse during the Dark Ages, but was put back into operation in the thirteenth century, when La Coruña became a major port. By the seventeenth century it had once again become a ruin, and it was not until 1785 that King Carlos III ordered its reconstruction.

Far left: *In the late eighteenth century, the original structure of the Tower of Hercules was repaired, then encased in a skin of granite blocks. At the same time, an octagonal second stage was added along with an octagonal watchroom and lantern, increasing the height to 180.5ft (55m).*

Top right: *The neoclassical façade conceals and protects the original Roman structure, although this can be seen from the inside of the building. There is an asymmetrical arrangement of open windows at each story, while "blind" windows give a geometric symmetry to the façade; the spiral relief feature encircling the tower is a reference to the ramp that would have surrounded the original Roman tower.*

Right: *The tower is perched high on a rocky headland that juts out into the Atlantic Ocean, warning shipping to keep clear of the rugged coast. Apart from its guiding lantern, the walls of the tower itself are illuminated by spotlights at night.*

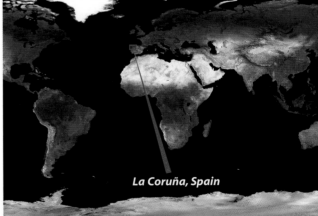

La Coruña, Spain

Tower of Hercules, La Coruña

· Foz

Arteixo · · Oleiros

· Lugo

· Lugo

· Santiago de Compostela

· Pontevedra

HERCULEAN LEGENDS

Many legends surround the Tower of Hercules, the most well known being that the mythical hero Hercules fought and killed a giant known as Geryon nearby. Hercules cut off the giant's head and buried it with his opponent's weapons, decreeing that a city be built on the spot. This led to the founding of the Roman city of Brigantia, which became La Coruña. In recognition of the story, the tower, and a skull and crossbones appear on the city's coat-of-arms.

Another story has it that the tower was built by the Celts and that it was so high they could see a distant green shore from the top. This prompted them to sail north and establish a Celtic nation in Ireland.

Utö Lighthouse

Utö Island, Finland

• **The big, square, red and white lighthouse on the Finnish island of Utö has stood there for almost 200 years, helping to guide ships on their way to the port of Turku through the mass of islands that dot the southern end of the Gulf of Bothnia.**

• **The lighthouse is probably the only lighthouse in the world that has also acted as a church.**

• **During World War I, the lighthouse was shelled by German warships, but they failed to destroy it. It also avoided capture by the Russians when the Finns repulsed a raid during the Winter War of 1939.**

Off the southwest tip of Finland is a maze of tiny islands, which stretch across the southern end of the Gulf of Bothnia as far as the Åland Islands. This area is known to Finns as the Archipelago Sea. The southernmost, inhabited island of this group is Utö, which lies about 37.5 miles (60km) to the southwest of the port of Turku. The island has few inhabitants, but, in addition to the lighthouse, it does possess a pilot station, a small harbor, a shop, and a post office.

To help vessels thread their way through the Archipelago Sea, a beacon fire was established on Utö as early as the mid-seventeenth century, the first such beacon in Finland. This was replaced by a lighthouse in 1753, but the round tower was blown up during the war between Sweden and Russia in 1808–09 (when control of Finland passed from the former to the latter). The present massive tower was erected in 1814, under the supervision of Chief Pilot Gustav Brodd.

Built on the highest point of the island, the stone lighthouse stands 79ft (24m) high, and has a large gallery and lantern, which displays a white flashing light. The lighthouse was the largest building on the island, and since there was no church, the islanders converted the third floor of the tower into a place of worship during the mid-nineteenth century, although the priest only visited the island twice a year. At other times, the islanders would listen to religious readings from an elder. The lighthouse also saw duty as a "town hall."

At first, the lighthouse was manned by two keepers, but after Russia seized Finland from the Swedes and made it an autonomous region, the number was increased to four. Temporary lighthouse guards were also hired and registered as apprentices so that they would be eligible to become full keepers when vacancies occurred. In the meantime, they made a living by fishing or other means; one was the village smith.

Far left: *The red and white vertical stripes, and the red lantern with its green metallic dome, make the Utö Lighthouse conspicuous in daylight from far out to sea, while its lantern provides two white flashes every 12 seconds at night. In front of the lighthouse stands an ancient fire beacon, a nod to an era when lighthouse technology was less sophisticated.*

Top right: *The walls of this most sturdy lighthouse were constructed from rough hewn granite, which gives its façade a roughly textured finish. Despite an internal staircase, a simple metal ladder runs up one wall of the lighthouse.*

Right: *In addition to the lighthouse, the small island of Utö is also the longstanding home to a pilot station. The yellow-painted building shown here, with its skeletal tower, was built in 1958 to replace an old wooden building that dated back to the 1840s.*

Utö Lighthouse, Utö Island

SWEDEN

FINLAND

• Tampere

• Saint-Petersburg

• Turku • Helsinki

ESTONIA   RUSSIA

Utö Island, Finland

WINTER CLOSURE

During the winter months, the Gulf of Bothnia freezes over, and until the 1970s and the widespread use of icebreaking vessels, it was closed to shipping. Consequently, the nautical lights in the region, including Utö Lighthouse, were switched off until the gulf became navigable again.

Vinga Lighthouse

Vinga Island, Sweden

- **The historic lighthouse on the rocky island of Vinga, off the west coast of Sweden, is not only an important aid to navigation, but also a major tourist attraction.**
- **Open during the summer months, visitors can climb to the top of the tower to obtain breathtaking views over the surrounding islands and sea.**
- **Built in the late nineteenth century, the lighthouse is one of several that have stood on the island, the remains of which can still be seen.**

The Swedish island of Vinga lies about 11 miles (18km) due west of Gothenburg, the country's most important seaport and the largest port in Scandinavia, at the entrance of the Kattegat, a strait that separates Sweden from Denmark. The island is one of the main attractions of the Southern Göteborg Archipelago, which today is a popular tourist destination, with a frequent boat service from the harbor at Gothenburg.

By tradition, the Vinga Lighthouse is the landfall light for the port of Gothenburg and, in fact, all of Sweden. Along with the Skagen Lighthouse on the Danish side of the Kattegat, it indicates the entrance to that strait and also the Baltic Sea for vessels that are inbound from the North Sea and North Atlantic.

The earliest lighthouse was built on Vinga in 1841, and some ruins of this tower still remain. It was augmented in 1854 by a second round stone tower, which continued in operation until 1890, when the present lighthouse was constructed. That second lighthouse still stands on the island, minus its lantern, adding to the historic interest of the site.

The current Vinga Lighthouse is a 95ft (29m) high, square tower built from granite blocks with an overhanging, medieval-style gallery. The lantern contains its original first-order Fresnel lens and displays a flashing white light. Close to the lighthouse is a large, red, wooden pyramid, which acts as a daymark and dates from the early nineteenth century. The lighthouse was automated in 1974, and around the tower stand a number of buildings that once provided accommodation for the keepers who looked after the light. One of these has been converted into a museum by the Friends of Vinga, a group dedicated to the preservation of the lighthouse and light station, which was formed when it became clear that the lighthouse was deteriorating following the withdrawal of the keepers.

Far left: *The distinctly medieval appearance of Vinga's lofty stone lighthouse tower is incongruously offset by the stark geometry of the brightly painted red pyramidal daymark that stands alongside.*

Top right: *Working in unison, the huge red daymark, surmounted by a tall spire and globe, and the lighthouse, are intended to provide invaluable guidance for shipping at all times of the day and night, in all types of weather.*

Right: *Vinga's sturdy lighthouse and daymark stand on this low-lying, rocky island, close to the remains of the 1854 lighthouse. The original round tower, now minus its lantern, has been converted to practical purpose as part of the complex on Vinga, which also includes a pilot control room, and various sector lights.*

Vinga Island, Sweden

Oslo

NORWAY

SWEDEN

Gothenburg

Kristianstad

Vinga Lighthouse, Vinga Island

DENMARK

Copenhagen

ISLAND ARTIST

Bleak Vinga Island was the childhood home of the famous Swedish poet, author, artist, composer, and singer named Evert Taube. The son of a lighthouse keeper, he was born in Gothenburg in 1890, the same year that the present lighthouse was erected, but brought up on Vinga. His home on the island is among the cluster of buildings that surround the lighthouse site.

Cape Hatteras Light

Outer Banks, North Carolina, USA

- **The Cape Hatteras Light helps mark an area of shifting sandbanks known as the Diamond Shoals. During the nineteenth century, before it was built, a large number of ships were lost in this region, which became known as the "Graveyard of the Atlantic."**

- **The conical tower is the tallest lighthouse in the United States, having a height of 198.5ft (63m), and it is one of several on the North Carolina coast that remain in use. When built, it was the tallest lighthouse in the world.**

- **In a major feat of engineering, in 1999, due to coastal erosion, the lighthouse was moved in one piece to safer ground, 2,870ft (875m) inland.**

The Cape Hatteras Light stands on Hatteras Island among North Carolina's Outer Banks, a group of islands that separate the coast from the Atlantic Ocean. Just off Cape Hatteras lie the Diamond Shoals, where the warm waters of the Gulf Stream meet the cold Labrador Current. This creates a breeding ground for powerful storms and rough seas that plagued mariners for centuries. A variety of lights has been employed in the beacon since it was built, the current device being a fully automated, 36in (91cm) rotating beacon of 250,000 candlepower. This flashes at 7.5-second intervals and can be seen at a distance of 23 miles (37km).

The current Cape Hatteras Light replaced an earlier lighthouse, which was erected nearby in 1803. The original tower came in for considerable criticism from mariners, who complained that it was not high enough and that the light was not bright enough; ship's lights were brighter and there was a danger of mistaking one for the lighthouse, with potentially disastrous consequences. During the American Civil War, the lighthouse was damaged by Confederate forces, and after the war, plans were made to replace it with something better.

Work on the new lighthouse began in 1870, under the auspices of the Lighthouse Board, being carried out by the U.S. Army Corps of Engineers. It took just under two years to complete and cost $167,000, being commissioned on December 16, 1871. At that time, it had a 27,000 candlepower light and a first-order Fresnel lens. Subsequently, a more powerful 80,000-candlepower light was substituted in 1912. In 1935, the tower was abandoned due to beach erosion and a new light erected on a skeletal tower farther inland. By 1950, however, following the construction of wooden revetments, the beach was restored and the tower put back into use.

Far left: *Due to erosion of the shore, the 900 ton Cape Hatteras Light was moved from its original location at the edge of the ocean to safer ground 2,870ft (875m) inland. The move was controversial with speculation that the structure would not survive. Despite opposition, the move was completed between 1999 and 2000 in a massive operation, and it was rededicated in 2000.*

Top right: *Because of its exposed location, the lighthouse requires frequent maintenance. Working on the 198.5ft (63m) structure is a major operation —even repainting its distinctive spiral black and white stripes, which are essential for the beacon's visibility during the daytime.*

Right: *Prior to its relocation in 1999, the Cape Hatteras Light— built in 1870 to replace an earlier light— stood in a vulnerable position, since the coastline of Hatteras island rapidly eroded.*

Outer Banks, North Carolina, USA

Cape Hatteras Lighthouse, Outer Banks

• Chesapeake

• Elizabeth City

Greenville •

• Ocracoke

• Jacksonville

A STRENUOUS CLIMB

Around 1.25 million bricks were used in the construction of the Cape Hatteras Light. The structure is maintained by the National Park Service, which allows visitors to climb the 268 steps to the top. The climb is strenuous, however, being the equivalent of twelve stories.

One of the vessels that were lost on the Diamond Shoals was the pioneering, American Civil War ironclad warship, the USS *Monitor*, which sank while under tow in 1862, with the loss of sixteen crewmen.

Vittoria Lighthouse

Trieste, Italy

- **The Vittoria Lighthouse in the Italian port city of Trieste is more than just a lighthouse. It is a monument to the Italian naval victory over the forces of the Austro-Hungarian Empire during World War I and a memorial to the sailors who lost their lives during that conflict.**

- **With its impressive, classical styling, the lighthouse is a noted landmark of the city, and it remains an active aid to navigation, guiding ships into the harbor.**

- **The tower is open to the public, around 200 steps leading to an observation platform just below the lantern, where magnificent views over the Gulf of Trieste and city can be obtained.**

Trieste is at the very northern extremity of the Adriatic Sea in northeast Italy. Following the Italian victory, the city and the Istrian peninsula to the south came under Italian control.

The idea of building a lighthouse in Trieste was proposed in 1918, but work on the lighthouse/monument did not begin until 1923. The tower was designed by the noted local architect Arduino Berlam with contributions by the sculptor Giovanni Mayer. The site chosen was the Gretta Mount overlooking the harbor. This had two advantages: it was 197ft (60m) above sea level and a solid foundation already existed in the round earthwork of the former Austrian Fort Kressich. The work was completed in 1827, the lighthouse being inaugurated on May 24 that year by King Vittorio Emanuele III.

The 223ft (68m) high fluted tower was built from stones quarried in Istria and Carso. Giovanni Mayer was also responsible for the powerful statue of a sailor that adorns the front of the lighthouse. Sculpted from 100 tons of stone, this figure is mounted on a plinth that also bears the anchor from the torpedo boat *Audace*, the entry of which into the harbor signaled the return of the city to Italy in 1918.

Far left: *At the top of the tower is an observation deck supported by a "capital." The former is referred to as the "crow's nest" in a clear allusion to that feature of a ship's mast. Above this is the bronze lantern, which has a copper dome decorated with a scale-like motif. Standing on the very top of the lantern is Mayer's beautiful copper sculpture of Winged Victory, which weighs about 1,540lb (700kg).*

Top right: *The construction of this magnificent lighthouse, which weighs some 8,000 tons, involved the use of 46,000 cu ft (1,300cu m) of stone from Orsera and Gabrie, 70,600cu ft (2,000cu m) of concrete, and 11 wagon-loads of iron, corresponding to 100 tons.*

Right: *The first Italian naval vessel to enter the harbor at Trieste was the torpedo boat Audace. Today, the anchor from that vessel adorns the Vittoria Lighthouse, below Mayer's noble statue of a sailor.*

Trieste, Italy

Vittoria Lighthouse, Trieste

- Verona   • Venice

- Bologna   • Ravenna

• Ancona

MONUMENT TO THE FALLEN

The Vittoria Lighthouse carries the inscription, "SPLENI E RICORDA I CADVTI I SVL MARE (MCMXV–MCMXVIII)" ("Shine and Remind of the Fallen on the Sea 1915–1918")

In addition to the anchor from the *Audace*, the lighthouse/monument also incorporates two deactivated shells from the battleship *Viritus Unitis*, which flank the entrance. The Austro-Hungarian warship was sunk at the end of World War I by a limpet mine attached by the crew of an Italian "human torpedo."

Westkapelle Lighthouse

Walcheren, Netherlands

- **The lighthouse at Westkapelle on the Dutch island of Walcheren is a major landmark of the small town and helps indicate the entrance to the Schelde estuary for ships en route to the Belgian port of Antwerp.**

- **The historic tower was part of a church originally, but the church burned down in the early nineteenth century, leaving its tower to continue as a lighthouse.**

- **Also known as the Westkapelle High or Rear Light, the lighthouse operates in conjunction with two other lighthouses, the Noorderhooft and Zoutelande, as a range light.**

The Netherlands has a long maritime tradition, and for centuries its coasts were dotted with beacon fires that burned on top of brick towers as a means of guiding its seafarers—the Dutch name for a lighthouse is "*vuurtoren,*" which means "fire tower." In the fourteenth century, one of those beacons was established on the western tip of the island of Walcheren, near the present town of Westkapelle. The island lies to the north of the estuary of the River Schelde, one of the great rivers of northwestern Europe, which empties into the North Sea.

In 1470, a large church was built in Westkapelle with a tall tower that quickly became a notable landmark. In 1817, taking advantage of the tower's height, a nautical light was installed, although the building continued to be used as a church until 1831, when most of it was destroyed by fire. Fortunately, the 131ft (40m) high, substantial, square brick tower survived. In 1906, a 39ft (12m) high, red painted, round cast-iron tower with a gallery and lantern was added to the top of the tower, the lantern containing a third-order Fresnel lens. The white flashing light can be seen at a distance of 32 miles (52km).

Far left: *In a unique marriage between an ecclesiastical building with a functional structure designed to save the lives of mariners, Westkapelle Lighthouse is an imposing sight. The red painted light tower protrudes from the top of the ornate brick tower, all that remained of the church after a devastating fire.*

Top right: *If the architectural style of the church tower was not proof enough of the building's former purpose, the graveyard still remains in the shadow of the immense structure.*

Right: *Reflecting its importance during World War II, the fabulous Westkapelle Lighthouse was listed as a National Historic Landmark in 1966, and in 2004, the cast-iron tower—rising some 39ft (12m) from the ornate brick church tower—underwent a complete restoration.*

WARTIME ROLE

During World War II, following the invasion of Europe by the Allies in 1944, Westkapelle Lighthouse played an important role in the operation of secret radar equipment, codenamed "Nelly." After British troops made an amphibious landing on Walcheren, a detachment of the Royal Air Force set up the portable radar equipment at the top of the tower, concealing the antenna beneath a box. Prior to the invasion, the dike surrounding the low-lying island had been breached by bombing to flood the area and drive out the German occupation troops. Most of the town was destroyed by the bombing and the floodwaters, and 180 of the Dutch inhabitants were killed. The floodwaters were considered a health hazard by Allied medical personnel, who insisted that the men operating the radar station could only stay there for two weeks at a time, all except one technician who was indispensable, so he had to stay permanently, fortunately without ill effects.

Westkapelle, Walcheren, The Netherlands

Westkapelle Lighthouse, Wetkapelle

- The Hague
- Rotterdam

THE NETHERLANDS

- Bergen op Zoom
- Eindhoven
- Antwerp

BELGIUM

- Brussels

Cape Reinga Lighthouse

North Island, New Zealand

• **Perched on the northerly tip of the North Island, the Cape Reinga Lighthouse was the last manned lighthouse to be built in New Zealand, being established in 1941.**

• **The concrete tower stands on a high, rocky headland overlooking an area of unsettled waters, caused by the meeting of the Tasman Sea in the west and the Pacific Ocean in the east.**

• **Of striking appearance, the lighthouse is well known throughout New Zealand, even though it is situated in a remote region.**

Cape Reinga is an important landfall for shipping making its way to New Zealand across the Tasman Sea and from the north in the Pacific Ocean. Although not quite the northernmost tip of New Zealand's North Island, it does mark the point where the two bodies of water meet. In 1879, the landfall was marked by the establishment of a lighthouse on nearby Motuopao Island, just off Cape Maria Van Diemen. This lighthouse served for many years, but was always plagued by the difficulty of reaching the island across the rough seas that are common along this rocky coast.

In an attempt to ease the problem of keeping the lighthouse supplied, a cableway was established between the island and mainland. From time to time, this even carried the keepers and their families across the churning waters.

In 1933, the wife of the assistant keeper was swept into the sea near the lighthouse and the radio operator dived in to rescue her, but both drowned. Five years later, the decision was taken to move the lighthouse to the mainland, and Cape Reinga was chosen as the new site.

The new lighthouse was built as an octagonal concrete tower. Eight buttresses reinforce the structure and provide support for the gallery and lantern. The latter was equipped with the lamp and lens from the Cape Maria Van Diemen Lighthouse, which was replaced by a small automatic beacon. In this form, the Cape Reinga Lighthouse offered a range of 30 miles (48km).

The lighthouse was manned until 1987, when it was automated; in 2000, the original lamp was replaced by an automatic, battery-powered flashing beacon, the batteries being kept charged by solar panels.

Far left: *Its white tower turned pink by the last rays of the setting sun and silhouetted against a dramatic evening sky, the Cape Reinga Lighthouse begins its nightly task of guiding shipping to their landfall in the islands that form New Zealand.*

Above right: *Although not open to the public, the lighthouse is a major tourist attraction; even in the 1960s, as many as two hundred people visited the tower every day.*

Right: *Cape Reinga is a high and rocky promontory, which places the tower's lantern 541ft (165m) above sea level. The range of its modern beacon is 22 miles (35km).*

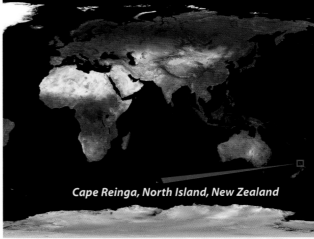

Cape Reinga, North Island, New Zealand

Cape Reinga Lighthouse, North Island

DEPARTURE OF THE SPIRITS

Cape Reinga gained its name from the Maori word "*reinga*," which means "underworld"; another Maori name for the promontory is Te Rerenga Wairua, meaning the "leaping-off place of the spirits." This refers to the indigenous people's belief that it is a place where the spirits of the dead enter the underworld on their way to the afterlife.

West Point Lighthouse

Prince Edward Island, Canada

- **Standing on the southwestern tip of the Canadian province of Prince Edward Island, West Point Lighthouse marks the western entrance to the Northumberland Strait.**

- **West Point Lighthouse is significant for being the first to be built on the island by the federal government, after responsibility for nautical lights had been transferred from the colonial government to the Federal Department of Marine.**

- **Although still an active aid to navigation, the lighthouse and former keeper's dwelling now house a museum, a bed and breakfast establishment, and a restaurant.**

Prince Edward Island is located in the Gulf of St. Lawrence, to the north of the Nova Scotia peninsula. It is separated from the mainland by the Northumberland Strait, which provides access to two important natural harbors on the island's southern coast, Charlottetown (the island's capital city) and Summerside. The West Point Lighthouse was erected on the southwestern end of Prince Edward Island to help guide shipping into the strait. Although it was constructed in 1875, the light was not commissioned until May 21, 1876.

The 67ft (20m) high, square, wooden tower, the tallest of its type on the island, stands on gray sandstone foundations which, in turn, rest on a layer of cedar logs, laid down to prevent the foundations from sinking into the soft ground. The tower tapers from 29ft (8.8m) square at the base to 12ft (3.6m) square at the top. The frame is clad with diagonal boards and shingles, and each floor has a window placed centrally in each facade. As was common with this type of lighthouse, a two-story keeper's house is attached to one corner of the tower.

Originally, the lens was rotated by means of a clockwork mechanism similar to that in a grandfather clock, the weights being housed in a long shaft that ran down through the center of the tower. There was also a special elevator for carrying fuel for the lamp to the top of the tower.

Far left: *The square, pyramidal design of West Point Lighthouse, with its attached two-story keeper's dwelling, is typical of Canadian wooden lighthouses built in the late nineteenth and early twentieth centuries. Prior to this shape coming into vogue, towers were either hexagonal or octagonal. The first two floors of the tower provided living space and were integrated into the keeper's house.*

Top right: *The lighthouse is painted in black and white stripes since it also functions as a daymark. Originally, the stripes were red and white, but the red paint tended to fade, making the stripes less distinctive.*

Right: *Standing close to the beach, this attractive and much loved lighthouse has an uncertain future due to the inexorable coastal erosion.*

Prince Edward Island, Canada

West Point Lighthouse, Prince Edward Island

Miminegash

Summerside

Charlottetown

Moncton

Amherst

New Glasgow

LONG SERVICE

Throughout the eighty-seven years that West Point Lighthouse was manned, there were only ever two keepers. For the first fifty years, the post was held by William MacDonald; between 1925 and 1963 (when the light was automated), Benny MacIsaac maintained the light. Both were local men, and today the lighthouse museum celebrates their lives and their dedicated contribution.

Maspalomas Lighthouse

Gran Canaria, Canary Islands

- **The soaring Maspalomas Lighthouse stands on the extreme southern tip of the island of Gran Canaria in the Canary Islands, off the northwest coast of Africa.**

- **The lighthouse is the most well-known landmark on Gran Canaria and dominates the popular beach area between Maspalomas and Playa del Inglés.**

- **The tower is the third highest Spanish lighthouse after the Tower of Hercules in La Coruña, and the Chipiona Lighthouse in Cadiz.**

Located in the North Atlantic Ocean off the southwest coast of Morocco, the Canary Islands are volcanic in origin. There are seven main islands along with a large number of small islets. The indigenous people of the islands, known as Guanches, are thought to have descended from the Berbers of North Africa. In the fifteenth century, the islands were conquered by Spain, and they have been Spanish territory ever since. Today, the islands are a major tourist destination.

As the port of La Luz, on the northeast coast of the island of Gran Canaria, grew in importance, it was realized that a landfall light on the southern tip of the island would be of great benefit to shipping approaching from the south. Consequently, in 1861, the decision was taken to build a lighthouse in the then remote region of Maspalomas. However, the structure would not be completed and the light commissioned until February 1890.

Because the chosen location was so isolated, it was necessary to send construction materials and men by sea, and before work could begin on the lighthouse, a small dock had to be built so that ships could be unloaded. The 180ft (55m) high, round stone tower supports a gallery and lantern, and its light can be seen from 22 miles (35km) out to sea. Attached to the foot of the tower is a magnificent and spacious, two-story keeper's dwelling.

Far left: *The magnificent Maspalomas Lighthouse looms high above the popular tourist resort and is a major attraction for visitors. When first built, it stood virtually alone in the remote southern part of Gran Canaria, but today it is surrounded by major developments, thanks to the boom in tourism in the island.*

Above right: *The tall, sllightly tapering, blue granite tower stands out starkly against the sky, and is a notable landmark for visitors and locals alike.*

Right: *As night falls, the lantern at the top of the lighthouse sends its welcoming beam out across the ocean, guiding shipping safely to their landfall in the Canary Islands.*

Gran Canaria, Canary Islands

Maspalomas Lighthouse, Gran Canaria

SHIPS OF THE DESERT

The vast sea of sand dunes that lies behind the beach to the east of the Maspalomas Lighthouse is popular with tourists who want to top up their tans in peace. For the more adventurous, however, particularly those with "Walter Mitty" tendencies, there is the opportunity to emulate Lawrence of Arabia by joining a camel safari among the shifting, burning sands. Unlike true desert travel, however, the chances of becoming lost are nonexistent, since the towering lighthouse provides a constantly visible landmark to guide such intrepid explorers and their "ships of the desert" back to civilization.

Rubjerg Knude Lighthouse

North Jutland, Denmark

- **Rubjerg Knude Lighthouse stands on the northwestern coast of the Danish island of Jutland, abandoned since 2002 due to the encroachment of massive, ever shifting sand dunes.**

- **Compared to many lighthouses, Rubjerg Knude had a relatively short working life; its light shone out over the North Sea for only sixty-eight years.**

- **Because of its unusual situation, the lighthouse has become a major attraction for visitors.**

Rubjerg Knude Lighthouse stands on top of Lønstrup Klint, a 196ft (60m) tall cliff that runs along the northwest tip of Jutland. When in operation, the lantern on top of the 75ft (23m) high, square stone tower could be seen from 26 miles (42km) out to sea.

Work began on constructing the lighthouse and keeper's cottages in 1899, the light station being completed in the following year, when the light was commissioned on December 27. The slightly conical tower had the appearance of something that belonged to a fortification rather than a lighthouse, and had a wide gallery at the top. Until 1908, the light was powered by gas produced by the station's own gas plant. Subsequently, gasoline was used as a source of power, but this was replaced by electricity in 1948.

Over the years, however, a massive sand dune grew between the beach and the lighthouse. Eventually, this became so high that it began to obscure the light from the sea. Finally, on August 1, 1968, the light station was closed because it could no longer do its job.

In 1975, the Vendsyssel Historiske Museum took over the site, turning the keeper's cottages into a small museum and coffee shop, but the sand dune steadily encroached on the old light station as it moved inexorably inland. Slowly, but surely, the sand overwhelmed the buildings, which had to be abandoned completely in 2002. Today, the ridge of the dune has passed the lighthouse and the buildings are slowly emerging once more from the sand, but, with the exception of the tower itself, they have suffered immense damage.

CENTENARY CELEBRATION

To commemorate the hundredth anniversary of the completion of the Rubjerg Knude Lighthouse, on December 27, 2000, local people organized a procession from the nearby church of Marup to the tower, where portable lighting had been set up to replicate the original character of the light. This remained in operation until the following New Year's Eve.

83

Far left: *Marooned in a sea of sand, Rubjerg Knude Lighthouse looks almost like the remains of a Foreign Legion fort in the middle of the desert. The abandoned stone tower with its battered lantern and faded paint gives stark testimony to man's inability to defy the forces of nature.*

Above right: *The accumulated weight of sand has destroyed the keeper's cottages at the foot of the tower.*

Right: *The Rubjerg Knude Lighthouse stands defiant against the surrounding dunes, but soon it will have to face the inexorable, more destructive forces of coastal erosion and rising sea levels, from which there is no escape.*

Lønstrup Klint, Rutland, Denmark

Rubjerg Knude Lighthouse, Lønstrup Klint

Skagen

Hirtshals

Hjørring

Aalborg

Thisted

Viborg

Men Ruz Lighthouse

Ploumanac'h, France

- **Men Ruz Lighthouse marks the entrance to the harbor of Ploumanac'h, a small port located on the northwest coast of France.**

- **Despite its appearance, the lighthouse dates from the mid-twentieth century and was built to replace an earlier tower that stood on the same site.**

- **The name of the lighthouse (also known as Min Ruz or Mean Ruz) means "red stones" in the Breton language. This refers to the pink granite blocks used in its construction.**

In the northwest corner of France is the province of Brittany (Bretagne), which lies on a rocky peninsula between the English Channel to the north and the Bay of Biscay to the west. The northern tip of the peninsula is known as the Côte de Granit Rose (the Pink Granite Coast) because of the color of the granite boulders that are scattered in profusion along the shore. These are at their most fascinating around the resort of Perros-Guirec, where they have been eroded into fantastic shapes. Large numbers of visitors flock to the area each year to see these amazing geological formations. They also have the opportunity to view one of the most picturesque lighthouses on this stretch of coast.

An old trail used by customs officers (the Sentier des Douaniers) leads along the coast from Perros-Guirec to the small port of Ploumanac'h, about 2½ miles (4km) to the west. As the port is approached, what looks like the remains of an old medieval castle can be seen on a rocky headland just outside the harbor. In fact, this "fortified" tower, built from the same colored stone as its surroundings, is a lighthouse, known as Men Ruz. Moreover, it was only erected in 1948. It stands 49ft (15m) high and is topped by a small, red-painted lantern that shows a red or white flashing light, depending on the direction from which it is viewed.

Far left: *Men Ruz Lighthouse with its battlements has the look of a medieval watchtower, surely the remains of a coastal castle built to defend the tiny French port of Ploumanac'h from marauding pirates and invasion from the sea. Alas, that is not the case. The solid-looking tower, built from locally quarried pink granite, was erected after World War II, during which the original nineteenth-century lighthouse was destroyed.*

Top right: *Outlined sharply against the cloudy sky, the lighthouse makes an eyecatching sight above the tumbled mass of pink granite boulders that are strewn along the coastline.*

Right: *As the waves crash against the rugged shore, the lighthouse stands defiant against the elements, soon to send out its welcoming beam of light.*

ROMAN WRECK

As testament to the dangers to mariners present along the rocky coast of Brittany, marine archaeologists have discovered the wreck of a ship that dates from the later period of the Roman Empire (between AD 100 and 300) 5 miles (8km) off Perros-Guirec. The ship was loaded with lead ingots, which have inscriptions that are similar to the names of Celtic tribes in Britain, suggesting that there was trade in raw materials in the English Channel in that early age.

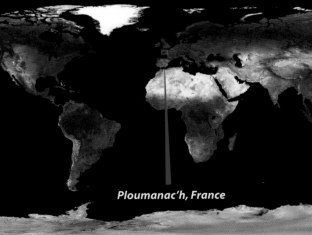

Ploumanac'h, France

Men Ruz Lighthouse, Ploumanac'h

- Perros-Guirec
- Morlaix
- Brest
- Saint-Malo
- Quimper
- Rennes
- Vannes

Pilsum Lighthouse

Emshorn Channel, Germany

- **The eyecatching, red and yellow Pilsum Lighthouse marks the eastern entrance to the River Ems on Germany's North Sea coast.**
- **Dating from the late nineteenth century, the cast-iron tower had a short active life and spent most of the twentieth century as an abandoned, rusty hulk.**
- **Today, the lighthouse has been thoroughly restored and not only acts as an aid to navigation again, but also is a popular attraction, guided tours being offered from time to time.**

Built between 1888 and 1889, Pilsum Lighthouse was erected to help guide shipping through the narrow Elmshorn Channel at the mouth of the River Ems, to the south of the German city of Emden. The 36ft (11m) high, round tower was constructed from prefabricated, curved, cast-iron plates that were bolted together. Unusually, no lantern was mounted at the top of the tower. Instead, because its purpose was to display a directional light, a window was provided in the side of the tower through which the light shone. A conical roof with a ventilator ball at the top completed the structure.

The lighthouse remained in operation until 1915, when the light was extinguished to prevent it from being of use to Allied shipping during World War I. After the war, a new, shorter channel was constructed south of Borkum Island, which made Pilsum Lighthouse obsolete. Even so, it remained in use as a daymark until the start of World War II, when it was abandoned completely. By the 1960s, it was in a sorry state.

The tower passed through the hands of several owners, with partial restorations taking place during the 1970s and 1980s. Finally, a complete renovation was carried out between 1997 and 1998, and in 2005 a new beacon with a 24in (60cm) lens was installed.

Far left: *Standing on a dike resplendent in its jolly paintwork, Pilsum Lighthouse has a comedic quality that endears it to all who see it. For many years, the tower was unused and neglected, becoming a rusted ruin. Following a complete restoration, however, it is back in operation, complete with new lighting apparatus.*

Top right: *Unlike most lighthouses, the tower does not have a lantern at the top. Instead, the light shines through a window just below its dainty conical roof.*

Right: *A pleasant pastoral scene enlivened by the bright colors of Pilsum Lighthouse. The striking paintwork ensures that the lighthouse is clearly visible as a day mark for shipping entering the River Ems.*

Emshorn Channel, Germany

Pilsum Lighthouse, Emshorn Channel

- Cuxhaven
- Norden
- Wilhelmshaven
- Hamburg •
- Emden
Bremen •

STARRING ROLE

The bright red and yellow Pilsum Lighthouse is one of the best-known lighthouses in Germany and, like the Westerheversand Lighthouse is a popular venue for weddings. However, the tower achieved fame not for its unusual architecture, but for the fact that it appeared in the 1989 film *Otto—Der Ausserfriesische*, a comedy starring Otto Waalkes. For the purpose of the film, the tower was used as Waalkes' home.

Cape Byron Lighthouse

New South Wales, Australia

• **The historic Cape Byron Lighthouse stands on a rugged headland at the most easterly point of the Australian mainland.**

• **Not only is the lighthouse the most easterly light in Australia, but it is also the most powerful, having a light of 2,200,000 candlepower.**

• **The lighthouse is a major attraction, receiving over 500,000 visitors each year. Cape Byron is also a popular site for watching whales.**

Cape Byron, a tall, rocky promontory on the coast of the State of New South Wales in Australia, was named by Captain Cook when he passed it on May 15, 1770. He chose the name in honor of the Royal Navy's Vice-Admiral John Byron, who commanded HMS *Dolphin*, which circumnavigated the world in a voyage of discovery between 1764 and 1766. It was not until 1826, however, that an exploration of Byron Bay was made by Captain Henry Rous of HMS *Rainbow*.

During the second half of the nineteenth century, a number of lighthouses were built along the New South Wales coast, but for many years a light was not considered essential at Cape Byron, since it was felt that the headland was clearly visible to seafarers. By the end of the century, however, that decision had been reversed and plans were laid for constructing a lighthouse.

Work began on the site in October 1899 and the light station was completed in late 1901, the light being commissioned in December of that year. The lighthouse was designed by the architect of the New South Wales Harbours and Rivers Navigation Branch, Charles Harding, who followed the ornate style favored by his predecessor, James Barnet. The 72ft (22m) high, round tower was constructed from concrete blocks made on site and rose from the side of a service building of similar construction. Close by were dwellings for the keeper and his assistants.

Automated in 1989, the lighthouse retains its original, French-made, first-order Henri LaPaute lens, which contains 760 pieces of highly polished, prismatic glass and is the only one of its type in Australia.

Far left: *The sturdy and ornate Cape Byron Lighthouse stands out sharply against the azure sky. This most well known of Australian lighthouses is well preserved and continues to operate as an active aid to navigation, marking the easternmost point of the Australian mainland.*

Above right: *The stout, concrete tower is equipped with a light that can be seen from a distance of 31 miles (50km) out to sea. The dramatic location of the lighthouse makes it a popular visitor attraction.*

Right: *The lighthouse looms over the crenellated service quarters and the surrounding buildings at Byron Bay, and dominates the skyline.*

A LATE ARRIVAL

It was planned to celebrate the commissioning of Cape Byron Lighthouse in 1901 with a great banquet. Many dignitaries were invited, including the premier of New South Wales, the Honorable John See, who traveled by government steamer to the site. Unfortunately, his ship was delayed by bad weather, and the banquet went ahead without him. The next day, fancy footwork did not prevent him from a ducking on landing and raised a cheer from the assembled onlookers. Subsequently, he presided over the christening of the lighthouse in vintage burgundy, which was not smashed against a wall, but savored by the party that had arrived by sea and missed the delights of the previous evening's banquet.

Cape Byron, New South Wales, Australia

Cape Byron Lighthouse, Cape Byron

Toowoomba •

Brisbane •

Nerang •

• Tweed Heads

Goondiwindi •

Balina •

Peggy's Cove Lighthouse

Nova Scotia, Canada

• **Peggy's Cove Lighthouse stands on a rocky headland marking the eastern entrance to St. Margaret's Bay on the southern coast of Nova Scotia.**

• **Although popularly referred to by the name of the nearby village of Peggy's Cove, in fact the tower's correct name is Peggy's Point Lighthouse, after the promontory on which it was built.**

• **The picturesque area is popular with tourists, and during the summer months, the lower level of the lighthouse becomes a post office from which they can mail postcards with a special cancellation mark in the form of a lighthouse.**

Nova Scotia, on the eastern seaboard of Canada, is connected to the rest of the country by a narrow isthmus, giving the province the appearance of an island. As a result, it has a long coastline compared to its area, and the rugged nature of that coastline has led to it being dotted with over 150 lighthouses. Around 27 miles (43km) along the coast to the southwest of the city of Halifax lies St. Margaret's Bay.

To mark the eastern end of the bay, in 1868 a lighthouse was built on a rocky promontory known as Peggy's Point, close to the inlet and small fishing community of Peggy's Cove. This first beacon comprised a wooden keeper's house with a lantern on the roof, and it remained in operation until 1915, when the present concrete tower was commissioned. Standing 43ft (13m) high, the eight-sided, white-painted structure supports a gallery and lantern.

The original wooden lighthouse building continued to provide accommodation for the lighthouse keeper until 1954, when it was damaged by Hurricane Edna and had to be demolished. Four years later, the lighthouse was automated and the Canadian Coast Guard withdrew the keeper.

Far left: *Peggy's Cove Lighthouse was built in the attractive, octagonal style common to many lighthouses in eastern Canada. Most, however, were of wooden construction, whereas this particular tower employed reinforced concrete. The sturdy building dates from the early twentieth century and is one of the most visited lighthouses in Canada.*

Top right: *The fully automated lighthouse displays a continuous green light from its red-painted, iron lantern, which sits 72ft (22m) above the sea.*

Right: *The pristine lighthouse with its sharp angles makes an interesting contrast with the jumble of huge rocks on which it stands. A lighthouse has stood on this spot for 140 years.*

St. Margaret's Bay, Nova Scotia, Canada

Peggy's Cove Lighthouse,
St. Margaret's Bay

• Truro

• East Hants

West Hants •

• Halifax

Chester •

Bridgewater •

THE NAME GAME

The community of Peggy's Cove was founded in 1811 by six families of German descent. There are several suggestions as to how it came by its name. Some say that since Peggy is a nickname for Margaret, it derives from St. Margaret's Bay, on which the cove is situated. Others are convinced that Peggy was an early settler at the cove. Another legend refers to a young woman called Peggy who was the only survivor of a shipwreck (some American families actually claim to be descended from this woman). It appears, however, that the truth has been lost in the passage of time.

Vizhinjam Lighthouse

Kerala, India

- **Perched on a rocky headland on the western coast of India, the striking red and white banded Vizhinjam Lighthouse looks out over the Arabian Sea, helping to guide vessels through these busy waters, many of the ships making their way to and from the Suez Canal.**

- **The lighthouse is not only an important aid to navigation, but also a major tourist attraction due to the proximity of the Kovalam beach resort. It is one of the most visited lighthouses in India.**

- **As lighthouses go, Vizhinjam Lighthouse is relatively young, having been built in the late twentieth century.**

Vizhinjam is a natural harbor on the western coast of India with a long history. Today, it is a small, quiet fishing port, but in the eighteenth and nineteenth centuries it was a bustling commercial harbor. Before that, the settlement played a vital role in the administration of the region. Currently there are plans to create a deep-water port with container handling facilities.

There is no evidence of a lighthouse having existed at Vizhinjam during its heyday in the eighteenth century, but it is likely that at least there was some form of daymark, such as a flagpole, to guide shipping in and out of the port. In 1925, a light beacon was erected at nearby Kolachal, while a daymark was erected at Vizhinjam in 1960. It was not until 1972 that the Vizhinjam Lighthouse was completed.

The 118ft (36m) tall, conical masonry tower was constructed on top of 70ft (21m) high rocky headland about 6 miles (10km) to the northwest of Vizhinjam itself. It supports a gallery and French-made lantern containing a three-panel revolving optic and metal halide lamp. The flashing white light can be seen from a distance of 36 miles (57km) out to sea. To make the lighthouse more conspicuous, it is painted with red and white horizontal bands.

The grounds around the lighthouse are open to the public, while the tower itself is open every afternoon, allowing visitors to climb to the top to enjoy wonderful panoramic views of the ocean, beaches, and mountains inland.

Far left: *Standing on a rocky promontory surrounded by windswept palm trees, Vizhinjam Lighthouse is an important navigational aid to shipping making its way along the western coast of India, and also to vessels heading for the small fishing port.*

Above right: *Close to the lighthouse is Lighthouse Beach, which stretches northward toward Kovalam. This beach is a very popular spot among tourists, many of whom take the time to visit the lighthouse, making it a favored attraction.*

Right: *Vizhinjam Lighthouse dominates the skyline above the rugged coast. The tower will play a vital role if plans to enlarge the port for commercial operations go ahead.*

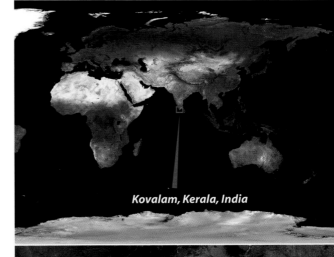

Kovalam, Kerala, India

Vizhinjam Lighthouse, Kovalam

- Madurai

Quilon•

• Tuticorin

Trivandrum •

ANCIENT FORTIFICATIONS

Between the seventh and eleventh centuries, Kerala was ruled by the Ay Dynasty, who made Vinzinjam the capital of the region. They built a fort to protect the city. In 2005, the remains of the walls of this fort were discovered close to the lighthouse. Built from large rocks held together with mud mortar, the walls had no provision for cannon, which was a useful clue in dating the structure.

Rethymno Lighthouse

Rethymno, Crete, Greece

- **Rethymno Lighthouse was built as a harbor light to guide vessels into the old port of Rethymno on the island of Crete's northern coast.**
- **Although it looks much older, the lighthouse actually dates from the mid-nineteenth century.**
- **The lighthouse was abandoned when a much larger harbor was built to accommodate the ferry traffic that serves the island.**

The island of Crete, today a part of Greece, is the fifth largest island in the Mediterranean. For many centuries, the islanders were subjugated by various foreign powers. After forming part of the Byzantine Empire, in the early thirteenth century, Crete came under the rule of the Venetians, who remained until the seventeenth century, when the Ottoman Empire took over. There was a short period of Egyptian control in the early nineteenth century before Crete was taken back by the Ottomans. It was not until 1898 that Crete became an independent republic, joining with Greece in 1913.

The third largest city on Crete is Rethymno, a historic port that has long played an important role in the economy of the island. Situated on the northern coast, between Chania in the west and Heraklion in the east, Rethymno was developed by the Venetians because it was well placed for trade with the rest of the Aegean and with the Arab countries. Much of the city and the old harbor was built during the Venetian period.

In the 1860s, a program of lighthouse construction was undertaken on the island, and as part of this, a tower was erected at the end of Rethymno's northern breakwater in 1864. Constructed of stone, the lighthouse is octagonal in section for the first two-thirds of its height and round for the remainder. This makes it look as though the upper portion was added later, although there is no record of this. On top is a lantern, now empty, and the remains of a gallery. The structure stands 30ft (15m) high. The lighthouse fell into disuse when navigational lights were installed on the ends of the breakwaters that surround the later outer harbor.

Far left: *Standing on the end of the thirteenth-century breakwater that encloses the old harbor at Rethymno, the lighthouse belies the fact that it was built 600 years later. The tower looks as though it dates from the same period. Most Cretan lighthouses constructed during the 1860s were the work of French engineers, although it is not known if Rethymno was one of them.*

Top right: *With its empty lantern and having lost the railing around its gallery, Rethymno Lighthouse presents a slightly forlorn sight. One day, perhaps, it will be restored to its former glory.*

Right: *At night, the old, abandoned lighthouse no longer sends out its welcoming beam of light to guide mariners safely home. Instead, it reflects the lights of the port in its honey-hued stones.*

Rethymno, Crete, Greece

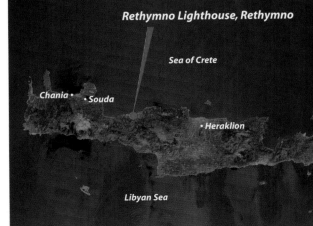

Rethymno Lighthouse, Rethymno

Sea of Crete

Chania • • Souda

• Heraklion

Libyan Sea

A HISTORIC PORT

The history of Rethymno as a flourishing port can be traced back to antiquity. Long before the arrival of the Venetians, it minted its own coins, which bore the image of two dolphins. Today, this tradition is reflected in the city's crest, which contains two dolphins within a circle.

Europa Point Lighthouse

Europa Point, Gibraltar

- **Europa Point Lighthouse is a historic tower that marks the southern tip of Gibraltar, a steep rocky promontory that overlooks the narrow strait that leads from the Atlantic Ocean into the Mediterranean Sea.**
- **Built in the early nineteenth century, the lighthouse is typically British in design.**
- **The lighthouse is operated by Trinity House, the British lighthouse service, and is the only lighthouse maintained by that organization outside the UK.**

Gibraltar lies at the southern extremity of the Iberian Peninsula, a tiny British enclave surrounded by Spanish territory. The promontory is dominated by the Rock of Gibraltar, a 1,400ft (427m) high limestone monolith that towers over the surrounding landscape. To the south, across a 15-mile (24km) channel that connects the Mediterranean with the Atlantic, known as the Strait of Gibraltar, lies North Africa. This is one of the most important sea lanes in the world, through which a quarter of the world's shipping passes.

Plans were made to construct a lighthouse to act as a landfall and waypoint mark at Europa Point in 1838, the task being entrusted to Trinity House, which was responsible for the lighthouses around Britain. The 58ft (18m) high, round stone tower was completed in 1841, and supported a gallery and lantern. Initially, a fixed light was displayed with a red arc that shone over the Pearl Rock, a dangerous reef to the west of the entrance to the harbor. Over the years, improvements were made to the lighting system and an explosive fog warning device was added. The power source for the lamp changed from oil to petroleum vapor and then to electricity.

In 1954, major alterations were made to the lighthouse, its height being increased by 6ft (1.8m) to accommodate a fixed red light immediately below the lantern. This shines out over the Pearl Rock in addition to the red arc of the main light, which flashes white and can be see over a distance of 22 miles (35km).

In 1994, the lighthouse was automated and the keepers withdrawn, although a former keeper lives nearby and carries out essential maintenance work when necessary.

GIBRALTAR
In AD 711, 7,000 Berbers landed at Gibraltar to begin the Moorish conquest of the Iberian Peninsula. They were led by Tariq, governor of Tangiers, who named the rugged promontory Jebel Tarik (Tarik's Mountain). Over time, the name mutated into Gibraltar. Although claimed by Spain, Gibraltar has been under British administration since 1704 and played a major strategic role in several conflicts since then.

Far left: *Sharply defined against a cloud-strewn sky and pristine in its white and red paint, Europa Point Lighthouse stands like a sentinel guarding the Strait of Gibraltar, one of the busiest shipping lanes in the world.*

Above right: *The lighthouse has been a vital aid to navigation through the narrow strait for almost 170 years.*

Right: *Perched on a cliff at the southernmost tip of the Gibraltar Peninsula, Europa Point Lighthouse makes a stirring sight, a solid and dependable structure above the crashing waves.*

Gibraltar, Iberian Peninsula

Europa Point Lighthouse, Gibraltar

Cádiz •   SPAIN   • Marbella

Algeciras •

• Ceuta

Tangier •

MOROCCO

Portland Head Lighthouse

Maine, USA

- **Standing on a picturesque headland on the east coast of the United States, Portland Head Lighthouse marks the entrance to Portland's busy harbor.**

- **Dating from the late eighteenth century, this historic tower is the oldest lighthouse in the State of Maine and the first to be built by the fledgling U.S. government. It remains an active aid to navigation.**

- **The beautiful setting of the lighthouse draws thousands of visitors each year.**

The rugged Atlantic coast of Maine is dotted with a large number of lighthouses. The pride of the state's lighthouses, however, is Portland Head Lighthouse, the oldest of them all, which has guided ships to Portland's harbor for over two hundred years.

By the late eighteenth century, Portland was America's sixth busiest port, but there was no lighthouse to mark the harbor entrance. A merchants' petition to the state government in 1784 and a shipwreck near Portland Head in 1787 prompted a scheme to meet that need. However, a lack of funds delayed progress until responsibility for the nation's lighthouses was assumed by the federal government.

A stone tower was commissioned from two local masons, the 60ft (18m) high lighthouse being completed in January 1791. President Abraham Lincoln appointed Joseph Greenleaf as the first keeper. He received no payment at first, being given the right to live in the keeper's house, and to fish and farm the surrounding land instead.

For many years, the light relied on oil as a fuel, but steady improvements were made to the apparatus. In 1855, a fourth-order Fresnel lens was installed; ten years later, the height of the tower was increased to 80ft (24.5m) and a second-order lens fitted. Eventually, in 1929, the light was electrified. The station was manned until August 1989, when the lighthouse was automated. Today, the original keeper's house is used as a museum.

Far left: *The light station at Portland Head, with its lovingly restored tower and keeper's house, makes a stark contrast to the rugged beauty of the rocky headland on which it stands. The tower dates from the early years of the United States and has become a steadfast symbol of the great nation.*

Top right: *Following the wreck of an English immigrant ship in 1864, the original tower, constructed from locally sourced rubblestone, was raised in height by 20ft (6m) and a stronger lens installed to improve its visibility.*

Right: *The beam from the Portland Head Lighthouse cuts sharply through the Atlantic fog, warning mariners to keep clear.*

Portland Head Lighthouse, Maine, USA

Portland Head Lighthouse, Portland Head

- Bangor
- Augusta
- Lewiston
- Rockland
- Brunswick
- Portland

FOR THOSE IN PERIL ON THE SEA

Despite the presence of the Portland Head Lighthouse, shipwrecks did occur from time to time, and the keepers were always ready to go to the rescue. On Christmas Eve, 1886, the British ship *Annie C. Maguire* ran onto the rocks close to the lighthouse. The keeper, Joshua Strout, and his wife managed to get a line to the vessel and all on board reached the shore safely. A few days later, the ship was destroyed by a storm; an inscription on a rock near the lighthouse commemorates the wreck. It is said that one early keeper used to keep a coil of rope near his armchair so that he was always ready to go to the aid of shipwrecked mariners.

Les Eclaireurs Lighthouse

Bay of Ushuaia, Argentina

- **One of the most well-known lighthouses in South America, Les Eclaireurs stands on a rocky outcrop in the Beagle Channel, a strait that runs through the archipelago known as Tierra del Fuego.**

- **The small, simple lighthouse dates from the early twentieth century and acts as a guide for shipping entering and leaving the harbor of the Argentinian city of Ushuaia.**

- **Being a harbor light, the lighthouse has a relatively short range of 9 miles (14km).**

Far left: *Les Eclaireurs Lighthouse takes its name from a group of five small islets, which lie in the Beagle Channel to the east of Ushuaia, the capital of Argentina's Tierra del Fuego region. Surrounded by the harsh, barren landscape, the wholly utilitarian lighthouse stands defiant against the elements.*

At the far southern tip of South America is a group of islands known as Tierra del Fuego (Land of Fire). The archipelago is split between Chile and Argentina, the border between the two countries passing from north to south across the main island of the group. On the southern coast of this island lies the city of Ushuaia, the capital of the Argentinian province. As with any island community, shipping is important in the region, and there are several beacons that help guide vessels between the islands and into the various ports and harbors.

About 6 miles (9km) to the east of Ushuaia in the Beagle Channel, which separates the main island of Tierra del Fuego from the smaller islands to the south, there is a group of islets known as Les Eclaireurs (French for "the guides"). These were ideally placed for the erection of a lighthouse to mark the entrance to Ushuaia's harbor. Accordingly, in 1920, a 33ft (10m) high, round brick tower was constructed on the most northerly of the islets, the light being lit for the first time on December 23 of that year. The height of the rock on which the lighthouse stands means that the light itself is 74ft (22.5m) above sea level. It flashes white and red, and is fully automated, being powered by solar panels.

Top right: *With a stunning backdrop of rugged mountains and high clouds, the lighthouse waits to point the way to the harbor at Ushuaia.*

Right: *Perched somewhat forlornly on its little rocky islet, Les Eclaireurs Lighthouse is a popular landmark among tourists who visit the region, and it is probably the most photographed lighthouse in South America. Boat cruises to the lighthouse are operated from Ushuaia.*

Bay of Ushuaia, Argentina

Les Eclaireurs Lighthouse, Bay of Ushuaia

Puerto Santa Cruz

Rio Gallegos

FALKLAND ISLANDS

Punta Arenas

CHILE

ARGENTINA

CONFUSING STORY

In Argentina, Les Eclaireurs Lighthouse is known as the *"faro del fin del mundo"* (the lighthouse at the end of the world). Many think that it is the lighthouse referred to by Jules Verne in his novel, *The Lighthouse at the End of the World.* That is not the case, however; Verne's story was inspired by the San Juan de Salvamento Lighthouse on the remote Isla de los Estados, which is still in the Tierra del Fuego region, but much farther east.

Fisgard Lighthouse

Vancouver Island, Canada

- **Fisgard Lighthouse stands on a small, rocky island just off the southern tip of Canada's Vancouver Island, at the western entrance to Esquimalt Harbour.**
- **The lighthouse was the first to be built on the west coast of Canada and has been designated a National Historic Site.**
- **Although the lighthouse remains an active aid to navigation, the attached, former keeper's dwelling is now a museum dedicated to lighthouses and their keepers.**

In the mid-nineteenth century, the territory that subsequently became the Dominion of Canada was in the hands of the British. On the west coast, Vancouver Island had a thriving colony of settlers with a busy harbor at Victoria on the southern tip of the island. Nearby, Esquimalt Harbour had been selected by the Royal Navy as a base for its ships in the Pacific. Because of the increase in marine traffic, it was realized that navigational lights would be needed to help guide shipping in and out of these two ports. The first of these would be built on a small, rugged islet known as Fisgard Island.

The lighthouse was completed in 1860, the light being commissioned on November 16 of that year. The 48ft (14.5m) high, round brick tower supported a gallery and lantern, the latter equipped with an English-made, fourth-order lens that could project a beam of light over a distance of 9.6 miles (16km). Attached to the tower was a two-story house for the keeper and his family.

The first keeper of the lighthouse was a Welshman by the name of George Davies, who sailed from England with his family on January 21, 1860. Their journey took over seven months. During a stopover in the Sandwich (Hawaiian) Islands, Davies discovered that the lens and other items of the lighthouse's lighting equipment, which was being carried by the same vessel, had been damaged. A replacement shipment turned out to be the wrong size, while yet another arrived damaged. Eventually, the apparatus arrived intact and the lighthouse became operational.

Far left: *Standing tall against the modest, white-shuttered, former keeper's residence, the stark, white-painted brick tower of Fisgard Lighthouse has watched over the entrance to Esquimalt Harbour for nearly 150 years. Since 1929, it has done so unmanned.*

Above right: *Mounted above the decorative corbelled cornice, the brightly painted lantern first shone the way for ships of the Royal Navy's Pacific Squadron, which used the harbor as their base. Today, the Canadian Navy is in residence.*

Right: *Fisgard Island is a tiny, rocky outcrop that lies just off the southern end of Vancouver Island, to the west of the city of Victoria. A causeway provides access to the lighthouse.*

WOMEN'S WORK

Shortly after starting work at the Fisgard Lighthouse, George Davies was called upon to help build the nearby Race Rocks Lighthouse. While he was away, his wife looked after the Fisgard light, making her the first woman keeper in British Columbia. However, this was not recognized officially and she was not paid. When the third keeper to be stationed at Fisgard Lighthouse, William Bevis, died on August 5, 1879, his wife continued to maintain the light until February 1 of the following year. Subsequently, she was paid the same wages as her husband would have received, making her the first official woman lighthouse keeper in Canada.

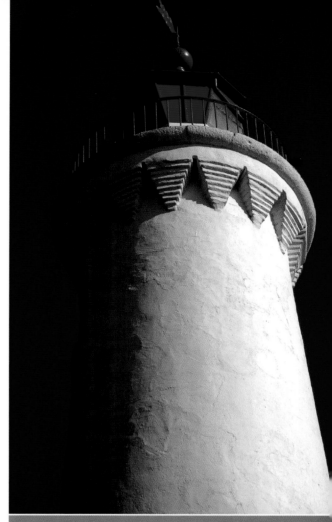

Vancouver Island, Canada

Vancouver Island

Vancouver •

CANADA

Fisgard Lighthouse, Vancouver Island

USA

Seattle •

Hornby Lighthouse

South Head, Sydney, Australia

- **Hornby Lighthouse marks a promontory known as South Head at the entrance to Jackson Bay and Sydney Harbour in New South Wales, Australia.**

- **The historic tower dates from the mid-nineteenth century and was built in direct response to two fatal shipwrecks that occurred in 1857.**

- **The lighthouse was named in honor of the family of the wife of New South Wales Governor Sir William Denison. His wife's father, Admiral Sir Phipps Hornby, commanded the Royal Navy's Pacific Fleet in the 1860s.**

One wild and stormy night in August 1857, the sailing vessel *Dunbar* arrived off the heads outside Sydney Harbour. The sea was too rough to embark a pilot to guide the ship into port, so the captain decided to ride out the storm. He was out of luck, however, and despite the best efforts of the crew, the ship was driven onto the rocks of Outer South Head in the middle of the night. No one on shore became aware of the disaster until the following morning, when the wreckage was discovered. There was only one survivor, an Irish seaman, who was found clinging to a ledge. Two months later, the clipper *Catherine Adamson* was wrecked off North Head; twenty-one perished, including the pilot sent out to guide her in.

The two disasters led to a public outcry and a demand for a beacon to warn vessels to keep clear of the two headlands. In response, the state authorities commissioned a lighthouse to be built on the very tip of South Head. Constructed from locally quarried sandstone, the round tower stood 30ft (9m) high and supported a gallery and lantern. Initially, the lantern was equipped with a kerosene lamp, but an incandescent gas apparatus was installed during the early 1920s. Subsequently, this was replaced by an electric lamp when the lighthouse was automated in 1933.

Georgian-style sandstone cottages were provided for the keepers. After automation, these were abandoned until World War II, when they were taken over to house army personnel and their families. The military finally left the site in 1977, and it was taken over by New South Wales Parks and Wildlife. A major renovation program was begun, which returned the tower and cottages to their former glory.

Far left: *The gaily painted Hornby Lighthouse, with its red and white vertical stripes, adds a picturesque, almost carnival-like, air to the rugged peninsula on which its stands. Designed by colonial architect Alexander Dawson, the little tower saw years of neglect after the light was automated in 1933, but it has been renovated and forms a major attraction of Sydney Harbour National Park.*

Above right: *The gallery surrounding the lantern features a delicate metal balustrade above the splayed cornice.*

Right: *Perched above a rugged jumble of giant rocks, Hornby Lighthouse stands on the very tip of South Head, guiding vessels heading in and out of Sydney Harbour.*

FAMILY CONNECTION

The first keeper of the Hornby Lighthouse was Henry Johnson, who moved into the keeper's cottage with his new bride, Mary Anne. Ironically, it turned out that Johnson's brother, James, was the sole survivor of the wreck of the *Dunbar*. The Johnsons went on to found a lighthouse keeping dynasty, many of their descendants entering the service in New South Wales.

Lindau Lighthouse

Lake Constance, Germany

• **The most southerly lighthouse in Germany, Lindau Lighthouse marks the entrance to the city's harbor on Lake Constance (Bodensee).**

• **The ornate tower is the harbor's second lighthouse and dates from the mid-nineteenth century. It took over from a thirteenth-century tower that still stands on the waterfront.**

• **The lighthouse is open to the public, who can climb to the top to gain wonderful panoramic views over the city and surrounding lake.**

The German city of Lindau, in the State of Bavaria, occupies an island near the southern end of the huge Lake Constance. The roots of the historic city have been traced to a Roman settlement in the first century AD, and throughout the centuries since, the lake has played a major role in communication and trade for the inhabitants. Today, the island is connected to the shore by a road bridge and railroad trestle, but its harbor still sees a lot of traffic, although much of it is for leisure purposes.

In 1853, the Bavarian railroad company (which operated ferries on the lake) began work on a new lighthouse at the end of Lindau's western breakwater, following the construction of a new harbor. The 108ft (33m) high, round stone tower was completed in 1856, the light being commissioned on October 4 of that year. Oil was used as a fuel for the light initially, followed by gasoline, and then gas. In 1936, however, there was a switch to electrical operation. In the early 1990s, the keeper was withdrawn when the lighthouse became fully automated, and it remains in use today.

This famous and much photographed lighthouse is still operated by the ferry subsidiary of what became the German national railroad, the Deutsche Bahn.

Far left: *The floodlit Lindau Lighthouse makes a dramatic statement in the darkness at the end of the western breakwater. Today, the beacon in the attractive tower can be operated on demand by vessels approaching the harbor, the light being switched on by means of a radio signal. Unusually, for a harbor light, the tower incorporates a clock.*

Top right: *The massive tower dwarfs its surroundings. It was built on the remains of a thirteenth-century wall.*

Right: *The narrow entrance to Lindau harbor is framed by the lighthouse on the western breakwater and a large statue of a Bavarian lion sitting on a plinth on the eastern breakwater. These icons of the city are favorites with tourists.*

Lindau, Germany

GERMANY

Ludwigshafen •

Lindau Lighthouse, Lindau

Konstanz •

• Friedrichshafen

SWITZERLAND

• Bregenz

INTERNATIONAL WATERWAY

Lake Constance is bordered on the north by Germany, on the south by Switzerland, and on the east by Austria, making it an international waterway. In the past, the lake was used by a considerable amount of commercial traffic, and all three countries erected lighthouses to mark the entrances of their various harbors. Today, Germany still maintains four lights, while Switzerland has two; Austria no longer has any.

Castillo del Morro Lighthouse

Havana, Cuba

• **The splendid Castillo del Morro Lighthouse looms over a rocky headland on the east side of the entrance to Havana Harbor in Cuba, lighting the way for vessels entering the port.**

• **Dating from the mid-nineteenth century, the lighthouse stands within the walls of an old Spanish castle built originally to defend the city and its harbor.**

• **The tower is the best-known lighthouse in Cuba and an icon of the capital city. It has been designated a National Monument.**

The entrance to the bay that forms Havana's harbor is narrow, and on the eastern side there is a promontory that is dominated by an old, stone fortress. Known as the Castillo de los Tres Reyes Magos del Morro, this bastion dates from the late sixteenth century and was constructed by the Spanish, who ruled Cuba until 1898, when it was seized by the United States. Designed by the Italian engineer Juan Bautista Antonelli, the fortress played a major role in protecting the harbor and city from naval attack; one of its defenses was a chain that could be stretched across the harbor entrance to a fort at La Punta on the opposite side. This effectively prevented ships from entering the port.

Although well built and provided with ample defensive artillery, the fortress had been planned to meet an attack from the sea. Consequently, when the British landed at Cojimar to the east of Havana in 1762, they were able to take the castle from the rear since they controlled the high ground. In 1763, the fortress was handed back to the Spanish, who promptly took action to prevent such a catastrophe in future by building another fort to guard against landward attack.

In 1764, a lighthouse was erected within the fortress to mark the harbor entrance. This stood for eighty years before being replaced by the current tower in 1845. Built from stone, the Castillo del Morro Lighthouse is perched high on the ramparts of the castle. It is a round, slightly tapering tower that stands 82ft (25m) high, and has a gallery and lantern. The height of the promontory places the white, flashing light 144ft (44m) above sea level.

Far left: *As the sun sinks in the early evening, it turns the stonework of the Castillo del Morro and its sturdy lighthouse a deep golden color. Soon the light will shine out over the sea to provide a welcoming beacon for mariners heading for the harbor of Havana.*

Top right: *The historic tower soars above the ramparts of the old castle, which dates from the time when Cuba was a Spanish colony and shows all the influences of its Iberian heritage.*

Right: *Standing on a promontory opposite Old Havana, the original core of the city, the Castillo del Morro Lighthouse makes a prominent landmark for those at sea and on shore.*

Havana, Cuba

Castillo del Morro Lighthouse, Havana · Key West · Matanzas · Corralillo · San Cristóbal · Cienfuegos ·

LIGHTHOUSE SCHOOL

Within the ancient Castillo del Morro there is a permanent exhibition devoted to the lighthouses of Cuba. The old fortress has a close link with the lighthouse service, since it once housed a school for lighthouse keepers.

Cape Florida Lighthouse

Key Biscayne, Florida, USA

- **Standing on the southernmost tip of the island of Key Biscayne in Florida, Cape Florida Lighthouse is one of the most well-known landmarks in the state.**
- **The light station is the oldest in Florida and has survived a turbulent history of wars, neglect, and storms.**
- **The present lighthouse is the second to stand on the site and dates from the mid-nineteenth century.**

Toward the end of 1825, Noah Humphreys completed the construction of a 65ft (20m) high, brick lighthouse at the southern end of Key Biscayne, the purpose of which was to mark the presence of a reef known as Fowey Rocks 4 miles (6km) offshore. Ten years later, the tower was attacked by Seminole Indians, incensed at plans to remove them to the West. At the time, the tower was manned by the assistant keeper, John Thompson, and an African-American, Aaron Carter.

The two men barricaded themselves in the tower, but the Indians set fire to the door. The flames spread to an oil tank and the wooden staircase, forcing the men to retreat to the top of the tower. There, the intense heat from the fire drove them outside onto the narrow gallery. Both were badly injured, Carter dying from his wounds and burns. Thompson, his clothes on fire, sought to end his misery by hurling a keg of gunpowder down into the flames. The resulting explosion failed to destroy the lighthouse or kill him, but it did dampen the fire. After looting the station, the Indians retreated, leaving Thompson for dead. Eventually, he was rescued by the crew of a U.S. Navy vessel attracted by the explosion.

Due to the threat of further Indian attacks, the lighthouse was not rebuilt until 1846. In 1855, the height of the tower was increased to the present 95ft (29m) to improve the range of its light. At the same time, it was equipped with a second-order Fresnel lens. This was destroyed by Confederate forces in 1861 during the Civil War. The lighthouse was repaired in 1866, but taken out of service in 1878 when a lighthouse was built on the Fowey Rocks. It remained unused for the next hundred years, but was put back into service in 1978 when an automated beacon was installed to mark the Florida Channel.

Far left: *Surrounded by swaying palm trees, Cape Florida Lighthouse is a major attraction of Bill Baggs State Park on the southern tip of Key Biscayne. The restored tower continues to act as a navigational light, marking the deep Florida Channel that leads into Biscayne Bay.*

Top right: *During restoration work in the early twentieth century, the classic, tapering, round tower was found to have foundations that were only 4ft (1.2m) deep, while beach erosion was threatening to undermine the structure. The construction of a new concrete foundation and revetments provided essential protection, but the tower remains dangerously close to the water's edge.*

Right: *The lantern and gallery is accessible to visitors who are prepared to climb the tower's formidable 119 stairs.*

Key Biscayne, Florida, USA

- Fort Myers
- Bonita Springs
- Boynton Beach
- Hollywood
- Miami
- Cape Florida Lighthouse, Key Biscayne
- Key Largo

AN EARLY SETBACK
The contract to build the original Cape Florida Lighthouse was awarded to Samuel Lincoln of Boston in 1824. He set sail in August of that year, taking the plans and materials with him, but he and his crew were never seen again; presumably the ship sank with all hands.

Bengtskär Lighthouse

Bengtskär, Finland

- **Bengtskär Lighthouse marks a group of small islands on the northern side of the entrance to the Gulf of Finland from the Baltic Sea.**

- **The imposing stone tower is Scandinavia's tallest lighthouse and dates from the early twentieth century. It remains an active aid to navigation.**

- **Having suffered from damage in two world wars and subsequent neglect, today the lighthouse and former keepers' dwelling have been renovated and serve as a museum, visitor center, and overnight accommodation.**

The many rocky islands and outcrops at the southwest tip of Finland have long been a danger to shipping entering the Gulf of Finland from the Baltic Sea, particularly those sailing from the north. In the past, lots of vessels were wrecked there. As a result, plans were made to erect a lighthouse on the islet of Bengtskär to warn of the dangers. The design, by architect Florentin Granholm, was shown at the Paris World Exhibition of 1900. It was not until 1905, however, following the sinking of the steamship *Helsingfors*, that funds were made available.

Work began on the massive lighthouse in early 1906, granite for the foundations and facings of the buildings being quarried on the island itself. Even so, almost half a million bricks were used. The 151ft (46m) high, round tower, with its 252 steps, rises from the end of a 3½-story keepers' dwelling. During construction, a time capsule containing the original plans and other important documents was sealed in one of the walls. Finally, on December 19, 1906, the light shone out for the first time.

The lighthouse was evacuated during World War I, the abandoned buildings being shelled by German warships, although little harm was done. Substantial damage did occur during World War II, however, and the lighthouse remained out of action until 1950. Following automation in 1968, it fell into disrepair. Fortunately, during the 1990s, it was restored and has become a major attraction operated by Turku University. As many as 10,000 people visit the lighthouse each year, 1,000 of them opting for overnight stays.

Far left: *Once the scene of considerable bloodshed during World War II, today Bengtskär Lighthouse is a major visitor attraction as well as continuing to function as an important aid to navigation. The keepers' dwelling originally housed the keeper, three assistants, and a machinist together with their families, totalling fifteen people. By the 1930s, however, that number had grown to forty following the birth of a number of children. In fact, there were so many children that a teacher had to be employed to look after their education.*

Top right: *A huge, 23ft (7m) long foghorn was installed in the roof of the keepers' house. When sounded, it made the entire building shake, but it could be heard over a distance of some 17 miles (28km)!*

Right: *For over a hundred years, the Bengtskär Lighthouse has stood on its tiny, rocky islet, guiding the many ships that ply the waters of the Gulf of Finland.*

Bengtskär Island, Finland

Bengtskär Lighthouse, Bengtskär Island

SWEDEN

FINLAND

- Tampere

- Saint-Petersburg

- Helsinki

ESTONIA   RUSSIA

UNDER ATTACK

In 1939, Soviet troops attacked Finland, and by 1941 had occupied the mainland opposite Bengtskär. The island remained under Finnish control, but the Soviets landed a force of a hundred men in the early hours of July 26, 1941. A battle ensued with the forty-strong garrison, who retreated to the upper floors of the keepers' house. Finnish artillery on nearby islands bombarded the invaders, as did Finnish naval vessels and aircraft, while the arrival of commandos finally ensured the defeat of the Soviet force with the loss of sixty dead. On the following day, however, the lighthouse was bombed, seriously damaging the living quarters and killing seven Finns. The building was not repaired until after the war.

Kõpu Lighthouse

Hiiumaa Island, Estonia

• **The ancient Kõpu Lighthouse was erected on the island of Hiiumaa in the Baltic Sea to mark the treacherous Hiiu Shoal and to warn mariners of the proximity of the mainland.**

• **This historic building, dating from the early sixteenth century, is one of the oldest continuously operating lighthouses in the world.**

• **The lighthouse is a major tourist attraction; for a small fee, visitors can climb to the top of the immense tower to gain breathtaking views over the Baltic and the Gulf of Finland.**

Estonia, once part of the Soviet Union, but today an independent nation, is a small country with a long coastline, being bordered on the north by the Gulf of Finland, and on the west by the Baltic Sea and Gulf of Riga. In the Baltic, there are two large islands just off the coast, Saaremaa and Hiiumaa. On the latter stands one of the oldest lighthouses in the world, the massive Kõpu Lighthouse.

In the late fifteenth century, the Hanseatic League, a group of Baltic Sea merchants, petitioned for a beacon to be built to warn vessels to steer clear of the Hiiu Shoal, just off the island of Hiiumaa, where a large number of ships had been lost. Work began on erecting a large, square, stone tower on the island in 1505, but it was not until 1531 that a beacon fire was lit on its roof. Uniquely, four large buttresses were incorporated in the structure, each facing in the direction of one of the cardinal points of the compass. In the mid-seventeenth century, the height of the tower was increased to the present 118ft (36m) to improve visibility, but it was not until 1845 that a lantern with an optical apparatus was installed. By then, the region was part of the Russian Empire.

By the late twentieth century, the tower was deteriorating badly, not helped by the use of the wrong paint during repair work. Eventually, the Soviet authorities were persuaded by the local government to carry out a proper restoration, and today the lighthouse is ready to guide mariners for many hundreds of years to come.

Far left: *The Kõpu Lighthouse, with its massive, triangular buttresses, makes an imposing sight. The original tower terminated just above the buttresses, but in 1659 the height was increased by the addition of a brick section, which can be seen quite clearly. A lantern was installed in the mid-nineteenth century, after the tower was taken over by the Russian administration.*

Top right: *Standing on top of the tallest hill on Hiiumaa and surrounded by swaying fir trees, the historic lighthouse dominates the skyline. At one time, the voracious demand for wood for its beacon fire caused the widespread deforestation of much of the island.*

Right: *This sturdy structure has stood for 480 years, helping to provide a safe passage for the many thousands of ships that have plied the surrounding seas.*

Hiiumaa Island, Estonia

Kõpu Lighthouse, Hiiumaa Island

SWEDEN

FINLAND

• Tampere

• Saint-Petersburg

• Helsinki

• Tallinn

RUSSIA

ESTONIA

THE WAY UP

Originally, the Kõpu Lighthouse had no internal stairway to allow access to the top. Fuel for the beacon fire and the men who tended it were hauled up the sloping sides of the buttresses with ropes. Subsequently, in the early nineteenth century, a flight of steps was cut into one of the buttresses and eventually roofed over.

La Martre Lighthouse

Quebec, Canada

• **The eyecatching, bright red La Martre Lighthouse looks out across the estuary of the St. Lawrence River from a steep hill on the south shore.**

• **This historic, wooden lighthouse dates from the early twentieth century and is a classic example of the style of octagonal towers that are found in many parts of Canada.**

• **Still an active aid to navigation, the lighthouse is also a major visitor attraction, offering a fascinating museum and guided tours.**

The Gaspé Peninsula, on the eastern tip of the Canadian province of Quebec, is surrounded by the Gulf of St. Lawrence and the estuary of the St. Lawrence River itself (the largest estuary in the world). This region forms a busy shipping lane that leads to the St. Lawrence Seaway and on to the Great Lakes. Most of the lighthouses in the province are dotted along this route to help guide shipping on its way.

On the southern shore of the St. Lawrence estuary is the town of La Martre, a small community to the east of Sainte-Anne-des-Monts. There has been a lighthouse here since 1876, although the present tower was built thirty years after that date.

La Martre Lighthouse is a wood-framed, octagonal tower that tapers sharply toward the top, where there is the usual gallery and lantern. Finished with clapboard siding, the tower is 63ft (19m) high, although the hill on which it stands places the light 130ft (40m) above sea level. Alongside the tower is a two-story keeper's house. The light station was commissioned in 1906.

At one time, the lighthouse was scheduled for demolition, but thanks in part to the efforts of its keeper, Yves Foucreault, the historic tower was saved and subjected to a major program of restoration. Of particular interest is the fact that the original clockwork mechanism with its cables and weights was retained and continues to rotate the heavy glass lens on its bath of mercury.

Far left: *The picturesque La Martre Lighthouse stands in a beautiful spot overlooking the Gulf of St. Lawrence, helping to guide shipping along the busy seaway that connects the North Atlantic Ocean with the Great Lakes. Remarkably, the well preserved lighthouse relies on its original clockwork mechanism to turn the massive lens that produces its characteristic flashing light.*

Top right: *Unusually, the beautifully restored and well-maintained lighthouse is painted completely red, whereas most other towers in the region are white with red bands.*

Right: *The historic lighthouse and its original keeper's dwelling were built on top of a steep hill and can be seen for miles.*

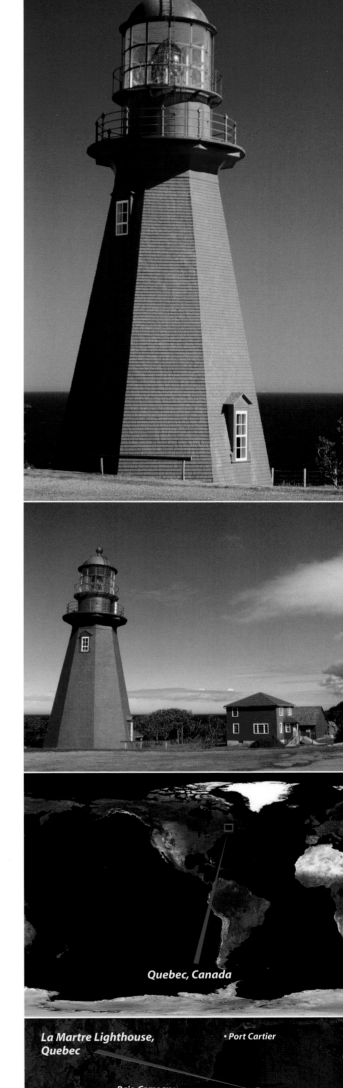

Quebec, Canada

La Martre Lighthouse, Quebec

• Port Cartier

Baie-Comeau •

• Jonquière   • Rimouski   Chandler •

• Quebec   Miramichi •

A COMMUNITY ASSET

La Martre Lighthouse and its associated buildings form the core of the small community of La Martre. The former keeper's cottage not only houses a small museum dedicated to lighthouses and their lighting apparatus, but also contains the town offices.

Westerheversand Lighthouse

Eiderstedt Peninsula, Germany

• **Westerheversand Lighthouse marks a dangerous area of shifting sands just off Germany's North Sea coast, to the west of the town of Osterhever.**

• **Built in the early part of the twentieth century, the massive lighthouse dominates the surrounding, low-lying saltmarshes.**

• **The striking tower is one of Germany's most well-known North Sea lighthouses.**

Just off the northern part of the Eiderstedt Peninsula, on Germany's North Sea coast, is an area of sand bars that are constantly shifting with the action of the current. Many ships ran aground in these treacherous shallows during the nineteenth century, so plans were made to mark the dangerous region with a lighthouse.

Construction of the Westerheversand Lighthouse began in 1906 on the low-lying saltmarshes behind the dunes that line the beach. To provide protection against flooding, a mound of the sandy soil was created on which the lighthouse could be erected. The ground was consolidated by running teams of horses back and forth over it and driving in a large number of wooden piles.

A single-story concrete base was constructed and then the tower erected on top from prefabricated cast-iron sections that were bolted together. The result was a 131ft (40m) high, round, slightly conical tower with a double gallery and lantern. Alongside the tower, two 1½-story keepers' cottages were built, one for the head keeper and the other for his assistant, together with their families. The light was commissioned in 1908, and the lighthouse was manned until 1978, when it was automated.

The lighthouse stands in Wattenmeer National Park, and one of the former keepers' dwellings is used by the park as an office. Guided tours are offered of the tower, the energetic having the opportunity of climbing to the top to obtain some breathtaking views over the surrounding landscape and out to sea. There is also an opportunity to examine a large Fresnel lens commonly used in many lighthouses.

Far left: *Assembled from 608 curved, cast-iron sections, Westerheversand Lighthouse was built by Isselburger Hütte. To stabilize the sandy mound on which the concrete foundations were constructed, 127 oak piles were driven in.*

Top right: *The huge, iron tower dwarfs the adjacent former keepers' houses. The red and white horizontal bands make the lighthouse visible for miles during the day.*

Right: *At night, the penetrating beam from the lighthouse cuts through the darkness to keep ships away from the treacherous shifting sands offshore. It can be clearly seen over a distance of 24 miles (39km), and depending on the direction from which it is viewed, the light shows white, red, or green.*

Eiderstedt Peninsula, Germany

Westerheversand Lighthouse, Eiderstedt Peninsula

• Husum

• Heide

• Cuxhaven

• Norden

• Wilhelmshaven

Hamburg •

HAPPY COUPLES

An unusual aspect of the Westerheversand Lighthouse is that it is often used as a location for weddings. In fact, so many weddings are held there that part of one of the original keepers' cottages has been turned into a registrar's office to record the many happy unions.

Imazu Lighthouse

Nishinomiya, Japan

• **Imazu Lighthouse was erected to mark the Japanese town's harbor at the beginning of the nineteenth century and stands on the quayside looking out toward the Bay of Osaka.**

• **The uniquely Japanese lighthouse remains an active aid to navigation, although unlike most lighthouses in Japan, which are maintained by the Maritime Safety Agency, it is managed by a private organization.**

• **The tower is the oldest lighthouse in Japan that continues to function and is an icon of Nishinomiya city. It was completely restored in 1984.**

In 1933, the Japanese port of Imazu, on the edge of Osaka Bay, between Osaka and Kobe, in the southwest of the main island of Honshu, was absorbed by the burgeoning city of Nishinomiya. The old town of Imazu belongs to the Nada district, which is famous in Japan as a region for brewing sake. In the early nineteenth century, as a major brewing center, Imazu had a flourishing trade in the export of the liquor to other parts of Japan, notably Tokyo (then known as Edo). Thus, the town's harbor was busy with the constant comings and goings of ships engaged in this trade, not to mention local fishing vessels.

To help guide ships into Imazu's harbor, the Ozeki Brewery sponsored the construction of a lighthouse on the quayside. Erected in 1810, the tapering, square, wooden tower has an integral lantern and a shallow, overhanging roof, and looks very similar to a Japanese garden lantern. The structure stands on a stone plinth and is 22ft (6.7m) tall. Originally, the lighthouse had a paper shade to help reflect the light toward the sea and oil was used as the fuel, but an electric lamp has been employed for the past ninety years, showing a green light to seaward. Thankfully, the historic structure withstood the Kobe earthquake of 1995, which devastated much of the region.

Far left: *The unmistakably Japanese design of Imazu Lighthouse combines elegance with function. The tower has stood on the quayside in the port of Imazu for almost two hundred years and continues to guide shipping into the bustling harbor. It is also a major attraction for visitors to the city of Nishinomiya.*

Top right: *The picturesque, wooden lighthouse was built originally to meet the needs of the many ships that entered Imazu port in pursuit of the sake trade. Today, while that trade continues, the surrounding industrialized region has brought a wealth of different cargoes to the harbor.*

Right: *Land of the setting sun. At dusk, the Imazu Lighthouse stands in stark silhouette against the darkening sky, ready to send a welcoming light across the waves.*

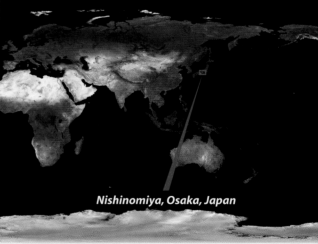

Nishinomiya, Osaka, Japan

Imazu Lighthouse, Nishinomiya

Kobe •   • Osaka

• Kurashiki

• Sumoto

• Kanonji

• Tokushima

Tanabe •

A LOCAL SPECIALTY

The Nada district grew to prominence in sake production for a number of reasons. To the north of Kobe, the agricultural conditions are ideal for the growing of Yamada Nishiki rice, the best rice for the liquor; the local Miya-mizu water is rich in minerals to produce a strong flavor; and chill winds blowing down from Mount Rokko to the north were used by early brewers to rapidly cool the steamed rice used in the process.

La Croix Lighthouse

Brittany, France

• **La Croix Lighthouse stands on a wave lashed rock at the mouth of the Trieux River on the northwest coast of France.**

• **The lighthouse is also known as the Trieux Front Light, since it is part of the Trieux Range along with the Bodic Lighthouse, or Trieux Rear Light.**

• **Unusually, the lighthouse has a distinctly medieval appearance, even though it was built originally in the late nineteenth century.**

The coast of Brittany is notoriously rocky and has seen the demise of many ships since man first went to sea in these waters of the English Channel. Glowering granite cliffs and treacherous outcrops that wait to rip the bottom out of any vessel that ventures too near make the area a potential nightmare for seafarers. Today, fortunately, the dangers are well marked, and many lighthouses dot these waters.

The Trieux River empties into the Channel through a long, narrow estuary between two large headlands, like the jaws of some giant mouth. Sailing into it requires skill, particularly from those who are unfamiliar with the area, since there are many rocks to catch out the unwary. To help mariners find the correct channel on their way to the ports of Lézardrieux and Pontrieux farther upriver, La Croix Lighthouse was built on a large rock at the mouth of the river.

Constructed originally in 1867, on the site of a previous eighteenth-century lighthouse, La Croix looks like the tower from an ancient castle. The 59ft (18m) high, circular structure is built from stone and has an overhanging castellated gallery, although there is no lantern. Instead, the flashing white light is mounted on top of a mast rising from the center of the gallery. Attached to one side of the lighthouse is a shorter and narrower tower that contains the stairs. To make the lighthouse stand out against its background, the side that faces the sea is painted white, while the gallery is red.

In August 1944, during World War II, the top of the lighthouse was destroyed by German troops under pressure from the Allies. It was rebuilt by the French in 1947, however, to the original design.

Far left: *The seaward side of La Croix Lighthouse is painted brilliant white for high visibility, and its name is emblazoned across the façade, should passing vessels be in doubt as to its identity. The lighthouse has no lantern, instead a mast rises from its castellated gallery, holding a light that flashes white once every four seconds.*

Top right: *The forbidding rock on which La Croix Lighthouse sits is just one of many that protrude from, or lie hidden just beneath the surface, of this dangerous waterway.*

Right: *The elegant structure was restored to the original plan after the top section was destroyed during World War II, and the newer stonework can clearly be seen in this view of the unpainted landward face. The secondary tower built against the main tower houses a stairway.*

SPACE SHUTTLE LIGHTHOUSE

Together with the Bodic Lighthouse on the mainland, La Croix Lighthouse provides an "alignment" so that vessels can be positioned correctly by lining up one light with the other. Like La Croix, the former was blown up by the Germans during World War II and completely destroyed. It was rebuilt after the war, and to make the cylindrical tower clearly visible during the day, a massive wall was built on each side, projecting above the top of the tower to create a giant arrow shape. This curious lighthouse resembles a space shuttle standing on its tail.

Trieux River, Brittany, France

La Croix Lighthouse, Trieux River

Cherbourg

Guernsey

Jersey

Perros-Guirec •

• Paimpol

Saint-Malo •

Yokohama Marine Tower

Yokohama, Honshu, Japan

- **The massive Yokohama Marine Tower serves a dual purpose as a lighthouse and an observation tower for tourists. In the former role, it is listed in the *Guinness Book of Records* as the tallest lighthouse in the world.**
- **The tower was built originally to commemorate the centennial of the founding of the port of Yokohama on the Japanese main island of Honshu.**
- **The lantern has a 600,000-candlepower light, which can be seen from a distance of 20 miles (32km).**

Yokohama is a leading commercial center in the Greater Tokyo area of Japan and one of the country's major ports. Originally, however, it was a small fishing village and only came to prominence in the mid-nineteenth century. At the time, Japan had just come out of a period of international isolation, having determinedly resisted contact with the West until Commodore Matthew Perry arrived in 1854 with a fleet of American warships and demanded that her ports be opened to overseas trade.

One of the ports that was due to be opened was the town of Kanagawa-juku on the important Tokaido highway between Edo and Kyoto. In the end, however, the Japanese were unhappy about its proximity to Tokaido and decided to build a new port across the bay at the village of Yokohama. That port was opened on June 2, 1859.

The port expanded rapidly and soon became the primary center for foreign trade in Japan. Resident foreigners were housed in an area of the city known as "Kannai," meaning "inside the barrier," which was surrounded by a moat. Yokohama's exposure to the West meant that the city received many aspects of Western life before other areas of Japan. For example, the first daily newspaper was published in the city in 1870, while the first gas-powered street lamps were introduced in 1872. Japan's first railroad was built between Yokohama and Shimbashi in Tokyo. Despite being heavily damaged by the Kanto earthquake of 1923 and again by American bombing in 1945, Yokohama rose once more to be a leading center for commerce.

When the city's centenary approached in the late 1950s, it was decided to commemorate the date with an observation tower from which the entire city could be viewed. Because the city was also a port, the opportunity was taken to incorporate a nautical light. The impressive, 348ft (106m) high, skeletal steel tower was erected next to Yamashita Park on the waterfront.

Far left: *Highly visible from seaward, and a valuable guiding light for vessels, the observation platform of the Yokohama Marine Tower also gives tourists a spectacular panorama over the city.*

Top right: *The lantern displays a light that flashes red and green alternately. The tower itself is painted in red and white bands, although at night its skeletal frame is illuminated with colored lights, predominantly red, green, and blue.*

Right: *Looming over Yamashita Park, the Yokohama Marine Tower supports a multi-story observation platform, on top of which is the lantern.*

Yokohama, Japan

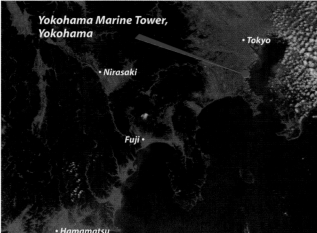

Yokohama Marine Tower, Yokohama

• Tokyo

• Nirasaki

Fuji •

• Hamamatsu

TEMPORARY CLOSURE

The company operating the Marine Tower as a tourist attraction went out of business in 2006 and it was closed, but the government of the city stepped in and has renovated the structure with the object of reopening it in 2009. Fittingly, that is the 150th anniversary of the opening of the port.

Port Adelaide Lighthouse

Adelaide, Australia

• **Today, Port Adelaide Lighthouse stands on the waterfront of the Australian port, an exhibit in a maritime museum, but for 116 years it played an important role in guiding shipping in and out of the busy harbor.**

• **The skeletal lighthouse served in two locations before finally being decommissioned and reassembled as a visitor attraction.**

• **Constructed from a mixture of wrought and cast iron, the tower was manufactured by the English company Moreland and Sons.**

Port Adelaide is the commercial port of the city of Adelaide, the capital of the State of South Australia. It lies in the southeast corner of the continent and has played a major role in the development of Australia.

In 1867, the components of the lighthouse arrived from England and were erected at the mouth of the Port River on a wooden platform supported on piles. The 82ft (25m) high, hexagonal, skeletal tower comprised a central cylinder containing a spiral staircase, which rose from a round, single-story keeper's dwelling, and a latticework outer frame that supported the gallery and lantern. The lamp was lit for the first time on January 1, 1869.

In 1901, it was disassembled and moved to Neptune Island, to the southwest of Port Adelaide, and equipped with a second-order Fresnel lens made by Chance Brothers. It was replaced in 1985 by a brick tower. Placed in storage initially, a lobbying campaign saw the historic tower restored and returned to its home port later that year.

Far left: *Looming above the waterfront, Port Adelaide Lighthouse is one of the South Australian Maritime Museum's most popular exhibits. The imposing tower provides visitors with a fascinating insight into the harsh life of the lighthouse keepers, as well as superb views over the surrounding port.*

Above right: *The prefabricated framework simplified the task of shipping the lighthouse to Australia. It also meant that subsequent disassembly and reassembly were relatively straightforward operations when the lighthouse was moved from one location to another.*

Right: *The iron framework supports an octagonal gallery surmounted by the lantern.*

Adelaide, Australia

Port Adelaide Lighthouse, Adelaide

Wallaroo

Port Lincoln

Murray Bridge

Kangaroo Island

A LYRICAL TRIBUTE

When Port Adelaide Lighthouse was relocated, a time capsule was discovered, containing the following poem, written by one of the Neptune Island construction workers.

When the sun doth gild the southern skies
Above these lonely isles
There is no need for this our lighthouse
Nor can't be seen for many miles
But when the storm and wind doth howl
Upon the ocean wild
The mariner will see this light
Which will beam out so mild
That fancy paints the lights of home
That cottage by the sea
Where dwell his loved ones all secure
From wind and wave while he
Doth work and toil to earn their bread
And die if needs must be
He then will bless this kindly light
And think mayhaps of us
Who built this light that such as he
Might rest secure while it flashed
Its rays across the sea

Sanibel Lighthouse

Sanibel Island, Florida, USA

- **The Sanibel Lighthouse stands on the eastern end of the island of Sanibel, which lies just off the southwest coast of Florida, opposite Fort Myers.**
- **Built in the late nineteenth century, the lighthouse was the first of many skeletal towers to be erected in the United States.**
- **The light station has withstood a number of severe hurricanes during its life. On occasions, these have caused the tower to sway and water to lap around the bottoms of the keepers' cottages, but the light has never been put out of action. They did lead to its automation in 1949, however, following concerns over storm erosion around the buildings.**

The crescent-shaped island of Sanibel is one of many that create an offshore barrier that runs along the western coast of Florida. It lies just off the mouth of the Caloosahatchee River, to the southwest of the city of Fort Myers. Today, the island is popular with tourists and is noted for the wide variety of seashells that washes up on its beaches.

The earliest settlers arrived on the island in 1833 and soon requested that a lighthouse be built, but to no avail. Within five years, Sanibel had been abandoned, however, due to disease and the sheer difficulty of surviving on the mosquito infested island. Following the Homestead Act of 1862, the island was resettled, and this time the residents' request for a lighthouse was granted, work beginning in 1883 at Ybel Point, the eastern tip of the island.

The new lighthouse was a 102ft (31m) high, square, skeletal, iron tower, with a leg at each corner and a central cylinder containing a spiral staircase to provide access to the watchroom and lantern. The cylinder stopped about 10ft (3m) short of the ground and was reached by an external staircase. Nearby, two single-story, wood-frame keepers' dwellings were built on iron piles. The lantern was equipped with a third-order Fresnel lens and was first lit on August 20, 1884.

Far left: *Many lighthouses have architectural merit, but the stark iron framework of the skeletal tower makes no pretence about its purpose. The Sanibel Lighthouse was the first of this class of tower to be constructed in the United States and has proved ideal for coping with the many storms that batter Florida's coastline.*

Top right: *At the top of the tower is a circular watchroom surrounded by its own gallery, and above that the lantern itself. Originally, this contained kerosene fueled lighting apparatus, but a switch to acetylene gas was made in 1923. Electrification followed in 1962, long after the light had been automated.*

Right: *The iron tower is a much loved landmark among the inhabitants of Sanibel.*

SANIBEL SALVAGED

The tower for the Sanibel Lighthouse was prefabricated in New Jersey by the Phoenix Iron Company and sent south by sea, along with the components for another lighthouse destined to be built at Cape San Blas in northwest Florida. When only 2 miles (3km) from Sanibel, the ship sank. Fortunately, divers were able to recover most of the parts, allowing construction to go ahead.

Sanibel Island, Florida, USA

Sanibel Lighthouse, Sanibel Island

Fort Aguada Lighthouse

Goa, India

• **Overlooking the vast expanse of the Arabian Sea, the lighthouse built within the grounds of Fort Aguada in Goa, on India's western coast, is the oldest of its type throughout Asia.**

• **The fort itself was constructed during the early seventeenth century by the Portuguese, but the lighthouse dates from the mid-nineteenth century.**

• **The old lighthouse remained in use as a guide for mariners for centuries, finally being decommissioned in the 1970s. Today, its place has been taken by a later structure.**

Located at the mouth of the River Mandovi, Fort Aguada was the largest of a number of forts built by the Portuguese during their occupation of Goa, which began in the mid-sixteenth century and lasted for 450 years. The massive fort, which stands right next to the sea and sprawls across the entire rocky penisula at the southwest tip of the region of Bardez, was built between 1609 and 1612 to protect the strategically located estuary of the River Mandovi, and thus prevent attacks on Old Goa by the Dutch and marauding local Maratha groups. It was a formidable bastion, towering 260ft (79m) above the sea and being equipped with thick ramparts, seventy-nine cannon, two magazines, two prisons, four barracks, a chapel, and a moat. It was the only fort never to have been overrun throughout the entire period of the Portuguese Empire.

From the beginning, Fort Aguada was a major landmark for shipping passing along the coast, and in 1864, the Portuguese constructed a lighthouse within the walls of the fort. This took the form of a 43ft (13m) high, round stone tower containing four floors, with a gallery and lantern at the top.

Subsequently, a second lighthouse was built a short distance away, to the west of the fort, as the rear light of a range with the original lighthouse as the front light. The later lighthouse is still intact and is a 69ft (21m) high, square concrete tower with a gallery and lantern. This lighthouse remains in use, being painted white with a red lantern roof.

When the threat to Portuguese India faded, Fort Aguada was converted into a political prison, where many dissidents and freedom fighters languished in misery for many years, suffering from torture.

Today, Fort Aguada is still used as a prison, although not for political prisoners, and it is the largest such establishment in Goa. Surprisingly, it is surrounded by a popular beach resort.

NATURAL SPRING
Fort Aguada gained its name because of a freshwater spring that rises within its ramparts, "*aguada*" meaning "water" in Portuguese. The crews of passing ships often would stop there to replenish their water supplies before continuing with their voyages.

Far left: *Long abandoned and clearly showing the patina of age, the Fort Aguada Lighthouse looks out over the Arabian Sea and the mouth of the River Mandovi. For centuries, the light at the top of this sturdy tower provided a guide for mariners, helping them find their way into the river's estuary.*

Top right: *The circular stone tower was built with a large diameter, which gives it a squat appearance, but this allowed the keeper's quarters to be incorporated. At the top is a partly open observation deck with an ornate stone balustrade and stairs to the light istself.*

Right: *The ancient stonework of the historic fort, which was once a bastion of the Portuguese Empire and essential to the defense of Old Goa, was never surrendered. Had attackers been able to enter, they would have had access to the vast reservoir, shown to the right of the lighthouse, fed by a spring that rises within the ramparts.*

Sinquerim Beach, Goa, India

Fort Aguada Lighthouse, Sinquerim Beach

Mapuca •
• Panaji
Marmagao •
Madagaon •
Hubballi •
Karwar •

Torre de Belém

Lisbon, Portugal

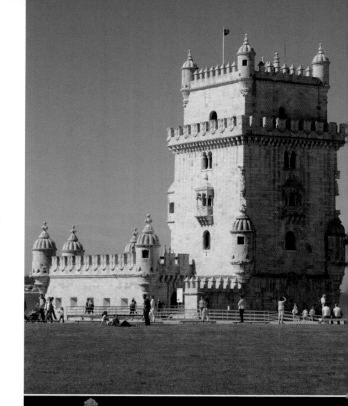

- **The Torre de Belém (Belém Tower) is a five-story fortified tower that was constructed during the sixteenth century as part of the defenses of Lisbon's harbor.**
- **During its life, the tower has had a variety of uses, among them acting as a lighthouse.**
- **The tower has been designated a World Heritage Site by UNESCO.**

In the sixteenth century, during what has become known as the Age of Discovery, Portuguese seafarers were roaming the world, and Lisbon, the capital of Portugal, was a major center of the international maritime trade. As such, the city and its harbor were potential targets for attack from the sea. Accordingly, King João II developed a defense plan for the mouth of the harbor that involved the construction of three fortresses. Two of these, Cascais, which acted as a lookout tower, and St. Sebastião da Caparica (on the south bank of the Tagus River and also known as the Old Tower) were built during his reign (1455–95). The third, the Torre de Belém, on the north bank of the river, was completed by his successor, King Manuel I.

The tower and its bulwark were built between 1514 and 1520, being located close to the point where a large warship had been moored to provide a crossfire with the Old Tower on the opposite bank of the river. The fortress was designed by Francisco Arruda, a Portuguese master builder who had made a name for himself by building fortresses in Africa. The work was carried out under the guidance of the Royal Master of Works, Diogo de Boitaca.

In 1807, the top two stories of the tower were destroyed by French troops when Napoleon's forces invaded Portugal, which led to the outbreak of the Peninsula War. Subsequently, the tower was rebuilt.

In time, with advances in artillery and defensive techniques, the tower fell out of use as a fortification, and over the centuries it served a number of other purposes. Among these were a prison, customs post, and telegraph office.

Far left: *The Torre de Bélem was built as a ceremonial gateway to Lisbon, and partly to defend the entrance to the Tagus river. In 1847, a navigational light was installed in the tower as an aid to shipping entering the harbor. Subsequently, in 1886, this light was transferred to a skeletal tower constructed nearby. The light continued in operation until the 1930s, when it was decommissioned.*

Top right: *The 115ft (35m) high tower stands behind the bastion, with its vaulted casemate (gun emplacement) and corner guerites (turrets) with Moorish cupolas, facing the river and providing a beacon for vessels at night.*

Right: *The guerites mounted on the bastion, here shown illuminated against the night sky, feature ornate sculptures of beasts; on one there is the image of a rhinoceros, reflecting Portuguese exploration of far-flung lands.*

Lisbon, Portugal

MANUELINE ARCHITECTURE

The Torre de Belém was built in the Manueline style, a distinctly Portuguese form of architecture with ornamentation inspired by the discoveries of the country's maritime explorers, such as Vasco da Gama and Pedro Alvares Cabral. The style was actually named in honor of King Manuel I, during whose reign it was developed. In fact, the tower is Portugal's only surviving example of a purely Manueline building.

Originally, the tower stood on a small island in the River Tagus, but, in 1777, an earthquake rerouted the river, and the island became part of the riverbank.

Vyborg Castle Light

Vyborg, Russia

- **Looking out over the Gulf of Finland, 75 miles (121km) northwest of St. Petersburg, the 165ft (50m) high main tower of Vyborg Castle is an ideal place to display a nautical light.**

- **The castle was built in the sixteenth century, although the island on which it stands had been the site of fortifications for over 200 years.**

- **The light is also known as Viipuri Castle Light and Malyy Shchit Range Rear Light.**

The castle at Vyborg stands on a small island off the Karelian Isthmus, in a narrow strait that connects Suomenvedenpohja to the Bay of Viipuri. Today, the island is in Russian territory, but when the first fortifications were built there, it was the easternmost outpost of the medieval Kingdom of Sweden. Subsequently, it became part of Finland.

In 1293, construction began on the first fortifications at Vyborg, under the instruction of Marshal Torkel Knutsson of Sweden. The island was part of Karelia, a region that was the subject of a dispute between Sweden and the Republic of Novgorod (the Russians). The stronghold was built as part of Knutsson's campaign against Novgorod, known as the Third Swedish Crusade, and was positioned to protect the Bay of Vyborg, an important trading site. The two states fought over the castle for decades, but in 1323 it was finally recognized as being part of Sweden.

The Swedes ruled over Vyborg and all of Finland for several hundred years, the present castle having been built by them during the 1560s. In the early eighteenth century, the castle was captured by Peter the Great during the Great Northern War. The subsequent Treaty of Nystad in 1721 gave Vyborg and part of Finland to Russia, and the rest of Finland was ceded in 1809. Subsequently, in 1812, Vyborg was incorporated into the autonomous Grand Duchy of Finland, which was part of the Russian Empire. Following the Russian Revolution and collapse of the empire during World War I, Finland declared independence, and the town became known as Viipuri. In 1939, however, Karelia was seized by the Soviet Union, but was retaken in 1941 by the Finns and German forces. The region remained under Finnish control until the end of World War II, when it was annexed once more by the USSR. With the breakup of the Soviet Union, it became part of Russia.

Far left: *Known as St. Olaf's Tower, the main tower of Vyborg Castle is square in plan at the base, then octagonal for the remainder, culminating in a green domed roof. A fixed white light is displayed through one of the upper windows to act as an aid to navigation. This is positioned at a height of 151ft (46m). Today, the castle serves as a museum.*

Top right: *An observation platform runs around the eight sides of St. Olaf's Tower, and visitors can take in the spectacular view of the city and surrounding landscape for a small fee. The building, foreground, is the Shoemaker's Tower, which in addition to being the castle treasury, nowadays contains a cafe.*

Right: *The castle complex contains numerous buildings, including the green domed Paradise Tower, left of picture. The main tower, painted mainly white for greatest visibility, has natural stonework at its base, beneath the level of the surrounding buildings.*

Vyborg, Russia

Vyborg Castle Light, Vyborg

FINLAND

Lake Lagoda

Helsinki

Gulf of Finland

Saint-Petersburg

ESTONIA

RUSSIA

Novgorod

TOWN ON THE MOVE

Vyborg Castle is the oldest building in northwest Russia. At one time, the town of Vyborg was contained within the castle walls, but eventually it outgrew the tiny island and was moved to the mainland nearby.

Low Lighthouse

Burnham-on-Sea, Somerset, England

• **Low Lighthouse at Burnham-on-Sea, popularly known as the "Lighthouse on Legs," is one of three lighthouses built in the English town.**

• **The lighthouse is a simple, 30ft (9m) high wooden structure perched on top of nine wooden piles driven into the beach.**

• **Despite its antiquated appearance, and the fact that it is over 200 years old, the Low Lighthouse is still in use as an aid to navigation for vessels in the Bristol Channel.**

Burnham-on-Sea is located at the mouth of the River Parrett, which empties into Bridgewater Bay on the Bristol Channel, in the southwest of England. The town is noted for its beach and extensive mudflats, which have posed much danger to both individuals and shipping over many centuries. There have been many shipwrecks on nearby Gore Sand.

The first purpose-built lighthouse in Burnham-on-Sea was erected by the Reverend David Davies at around 1800. He had a four-story round tower constructed just behind the beach. At first, this was maintained through the voluntary contributions of local merchants and ship owners, but eventually Davies was given the right to levy a charge on all vessels entering the nearby port of Bridgewater.

In 1829, responsibility for Davies' lighthouse passed to Trinity House, the organization set up to run all lighthouses in England. They kept it in operation for three years until 1832, when a new, taller, pillar lighthouse was built. The 99ft (30m) high brick tower had a kerosene fired light, but it was soon realized that the massive tidal range of the Bristol Channel (as much as 40ft/12m) meant that the selected vantage point was too low. Consequently, the wooden lighthouse was built on the beach so that it would be more visible. It is likely that the two lighthouses were intended to be leading lights, allowing mariners to line them up to obtain a compass bearing.

Low Lighthouse was also completed in 1832, and it remained in use until well into the twentieth century. It was taken out of commission in 1969, but was put back in use in 1993, when the pillar lighthouse was decommissioned. Today, Low Lighthouse displays a white flashing light and a directional light, which shows white, red, or green, depending on the direction from which it is viewed.

Far left: *Low Lighthouse still fulfills its role as a leading light, in conjunction with a nearby brick pillar beacon, now a private home, enabling mariners to obtain a compass bearing. The distinctive two-story structure is wood framed, with clapboard siding, and is accessible on foot only when the tide is out.*

Top right: *The sun rises behind the lighthouse, casting long shadows through its nine wooden supporting legs. The building is painted white for highest visibility from the sea, with a distinctive vertical red stripe on its seaward elevation.*

Right: *A moment of quiet reflection as the sun sinks below the horizon, the lonely but quaintly eccentric figure of Low Lighthouse stands as if marooned on the broad beach. The humble structure, however, performs an important function for the safety of those at sea.*

Burnham-on-Sea, England

Low Lighthouse, Burnham-on-Sea

• London
• Bristol
• Weston-super-mare
Minehead •
• Portsmouth
• Exeter

English Channel

KEEPING A CANDLE BURNING

The history of lighthouses in Burnham-on-Sea began one stormy night around 1750, when the wife of a local fisherman placed a candle in the window of their cottage to guide her husband home. Other fishermen were so impressed that they began paying her to keep the candle burning for the benefit of the local fleet. Subsequently, the sexton of the adjacent church took over her role and placed a light on the church tower, which, being higher, could be seen from a greater distance.

Thomas Point Shoal Lighthouse

Chesapeake Bay, Maryland, USA

• **For over 130 years, the historic Thomas Point Shoal Lighthouse has stood in Chesapeake Bay, marking a dangerous shoal near the mouth of the South River.**

• **The only unaltered example of a cottage screwpile lighthouse remaining in the United States on its original foundations, the lighthouse has been designated a National Historic Landmark, one of only nine U.S. lighthouses to be so honored.**

• **The lighthouse was saved from demolition in 1972 by a public campaign and taken into the ownership of the city of Annapolis, although the Coast Guard continues to maintain the light.**

The Thomas Point Shoal is an area of shallow water that extends out into Chesapeake Bay for a distance of 1.25 miles (2km). It lies to the south of the city of Annapolis, presenting a danger to vessels passing through the bay. In 1872, the U.S. Lighthouse Board realized that there was a need to site a lighthouse on the shoal in place of an inadequate, shore-based beacon. Although the board had erected inexpensive screwpile lighthouses elsewhere in the bay, several had been overwhelmed by icefields, so its preference was for a stronger caisson design. However, insufficient funding meant that a screwpile structure was the only realistic option.

The hexagonal, 1½-story, wooden, cottage-style lighthouse stands on seven screwpiles, one at each corner and one in the center. It has a diameter of 35ft (11m). A lantern and gallery are mounted on the roof, being equipped with a solar powered lens following automation in 1986. The light is 43ft (13m) above the water and can be seen at a distance of 11 miles (18km).

In the winter of 1877, thick ice sheets damaged the lighthouse. To provide future protection, an "ice breaker" was constructed from steel piles driven into the bed of the bay immediately to the north of the lighthouse. Over the years, these have been reinforced by large quantities of stone.

Far left: *A glimpse of the past. The quaint Thomas Point Shoal Lighthouse has been warning shipping in Chesapeake Bay to steer clear of the dangerous shallows near the mouth of the South River since 1875. The piles of rock on each side are there to protect the historic screwpile lighthouse from winter ice, which once toppled and broke the lens of the light.*

Above right: *The fragile looking structure is remarkably resilient, having withstood the crushing ice of harsh winters and the violent seas of tropical storms. No longer manned, from time to time it is opened to guided tours.*

Right: *Silhouetted by a glorious sunset, the lighthouse stands ready to do its duty once more.*

MAROONED

The first lighthouse marking the Thomas Point Shoal was built on shore in 1824. A 30ft (9m) high, stone tower was erected on a high bluff, 100ft (30m) from the water's edge. Within fourteen years, however, erosion had cut the distance to 15ft (4.5m). The tower was rebuilt farther inland, but there were constant doubts about its effectiveness, and eventually it was replaced by the screwpile structure. As time passed, the waters of the bay broke through the headland on which the old tower stood, isolating the light station on a tiny island. In 1894, the lighthouse finally succumbed and toppled into the bay.

Chesapeake Bay, Maryland, USA

Thomas Point Shoal Lighthouse, Chesapeake Bay

• Baltimore

• Annapolis

Washington •

Deale • • Easton

• Frederiksburg

Heceta Head Lighthouse

Florence, Oregon, USA

• **The most powerful lighthouse in the State of Oregon, Heceta Head can be seen from 21 miles (34km) out to sea and has been guiding shipping since 1894.**

• **The historic tower is perched on a remote, steep, rocky promontory overlooking the Pacific Ocean, and is surrounded by the tall, fragrant pines and spruce of the Siuslaw National Forest.**

• **Listed in the National Register of Historic Places, the lighthouse attracts thousands of visitors each year.**

Heceta Head takes its name from Don Bruno Heceta, a Portuguese navigator in the employ of the Spanish, who set out from Mexico in 1775 to follow the Pacific Coast north to the Arctic Circle, claiming territory for Spain as he went. He only made it as far as the Columbia River, however, before sickness among his crew forced him to turn back. On his journey, he had given the prominent headland his name.

Work began on the construction of the lighthouse at Heceta Head in 1892, using local lumber, while other building materials were shipped in from San Francisco; the foundation for the tower was created from rock quarried near Oregon City. The construction crew took two years to complete the task, laborers being paid $2 a day for a ten-hour shift.

The brick tower stands 56ft (17m) high, and supports a gallery and lantern with a first-order Fresnel lens. Attached to the tower is a single-story workshop. A single dwelling was provided for the head keeper and his family, while a duplex was built for the assistant keepers. Subsequently, the head keeper's house was demolished, but the assistant keeper's accommodation has been preserved, as have two former oil buildings and a garage.

Originally, the lens was turned by a clockwork mechanism, but today an electric motor handles that task. On February 12, 1961, a landslide cut off the electricity supply to the lighthouse and then the standby generator failed. To maintain the light, the keepers resorted to an oil lamp and turned the lens by hand, walking continuously around the lamp room for over seven hours. Two years later, the lighthouse was fully automated and the keepers withdrawn.

Far left: *The Heceta Head Lighthouse is still equipped with its original, massive, first-order Fresnel lens, which was made by the Chance brothers in England in the late nineteenth century. This throws a powerful beam of light out to sea to help shipping find its way along the rugged Oregon coast.*

Above right: *Now under the ownership of Oregon State Parks, the lighthouse and its surrounding buildings have been preserved and are major tourist attractions. The picturesque spot is popular for watching gray whales, sealions, and nesting seabirds.*

Right: *Located about 12 miles (19km) from the town of Florence, the lighthouse occupies an isolated position on a rocky headland among the breathtaking beauty of the Siuslaw National Forest.*

Florence, Oregon, USA

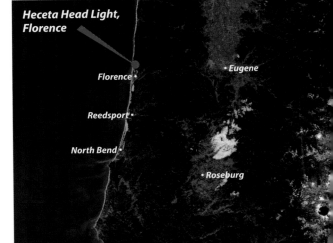

Heceta Head Light, Florence

Florence •   • Eugene

Reedsport •

North Bend •

• Roseburg

GHOSTLY GOINGS-ON

Heceta House, the former assistant keepers' dwelling now used as an interpretive center and bed and breakfast accommodation, is considered to be one of the ten most haunted houses in the United States. Fortunately for the vistors, the ghost, a female by the name of Rue, is mischievous rather than malevolent. She has been known to sweep up broken glass and exchange a silk stocking for rat poison.

Holland Harbor Lighthouse

Lake Michigan, USA

• **Holland Harbor Lighthouse was built originally to house a steam powered fog signal, but in the mid-1930s, a tower and lantern were added to create a lighthouse.**

• **The lighthouse marks the entrance to a channel that connects Lake Michigan to Lake Macatawa, at the southeast end of which is the city of Holland. It is also known as the South Pierhead Light.**

• **Although once threatened with demolition, the lighthouse has been preserved and is listed on the National Register of Historic Places.**

In 1847, when Dutch settlers arrived at Black Lake on the eastern shore of Lake Michigan, they immediately saw the potential of using the lake as a harbor for a new settlement, which they named Holland after their homeland. Black Lake, subsequently renamed Lake Macatawa, was a broadening of the Black River where it fed into the vast lake. The only problem was that the channel between the two lakes had silted up. The settlers appealed to Congress for help to dredge the channel, but were ignored and eventually took on the task themselves. On July 1, 1859, the steamer *Huron* became the first major vessel to enter the new port.

In 1869, Federal aid arrived in the shape of the Army Corps of Engineers, who improved the channel and added two piers extending out into Lake Michigan. In the following year, a pyramidal beacon was established at the end of the south pier. In 1890, a lantern was erected on a post at the outer end of the pier to act as a front range light for the existing beacon.

By the turn of the twentieth century, Holland had become a major vacation destination, and traffic in and out of the harbor had grown considerably. Because of this, in 1907, a fog signal building was erected. On the first floor was a 10in (25cm) steam whistle and its boiler. These were replaced by an electric/air operated whistle in 1933, a year after the pierhead light had been electrified.

In 1936, a square tower was added to the building to support an octagonal lantern, while the pierhead beacon was removed. In this form, the lighthouse continued to guide shipping into the harbor, but in 1972 the Coast Guard indicated that they wanted to abandon the building because of high maintenance costs. A local outcry led to the formation of the Holland Harbor Lighthouse Commission in 1974. The commission took over responsibility for the structure and continues to maintain it to this day.

Far left: *Constructed near the end of the south pier, the wood-frame fog-signal building was clad with iron sheets and had accommodation in the twin gabled roof for two assistant keepers. The square tower was added three years later to support an octagonal lantern.*

Top right: *"Big Red" proudly displays the U.S. flag from its 32ft (9.7m) high tower. The building resembles a traditional Dutch gable-roofed house, apart from its lack of windows and doors. It is virtually identical to the Kewaunee Pierhead Light on the Wisconsin side of Lake Michigan—apart from the bold red color that gives it its popular nickname.*

Right: *From the park, a good view of "Big Red" can be obtained from the opposite side to the entrance to Lake Macatawa. For a closer look, it is necessary to visit the south side of the lake entrance; the area is mainly private property, although limited public access is permitted, and a lengthy walk called for. The lighthouse itself is not open to the public.*

BIG RED

The Holland Harbor Lighthouse is painted bright red. This was done originally in accordance with Coast Guard regulations, which required that any navigational beacon on the right of a harbor entrance be that color. The distinctive finish has given rise to the lighthouse's popular local name: "Big Red."

Lake Michigan, USA

Holland Harbor Lighthouse, Lake Michigan

• *Grand Rapids*

• *Holland*

Lake Michigan

• *Kalamazoo*

Kennewick •

• *Chicago*

Cape Bonavista Lighthouse

Newfoundland, Canada

• **Standing on the wild and rugged coastline of Newfoundland, Cape Bonavista Lighthouse played a major role in safeguarding the lives of seafarers for over 120 years.**

• **No longer operational, the historic lighthouse is now a museum, providing a fascinating insight into the lives of the dedicated men and women who maintained the world's nautical lights in the days before automation.**

• **The lighthouse has been designated a Provincial Historic Site by the Canadian government.**

Newfoundland is a large island off the east coast of Canada. In the early days of exploration and navigation in the region, a large number of vessels came to grief on its rocky, jagged coastline. This led to the establishment of many lighthouses around the island. On the northeast coast of Newfoundland is Cape Bonavista, a headland that juts out into the North Atlantic. On this exposed point, the Atlantic waves crash against the rocks, ready to hurl any vessel that comes too close to destruction. The cape is widely regarded as the spot where the Italian navigator John Cabot made landfall on June 24, 1497, to discover the North American mainland, and a statue nearby pays tribute to that belief.

In early 1841, Newfoundland's House of Assembly agreed to the construction of a lighthouse at Cape Bonavista, and construction began later the same year. The building took two years to complete, the light being commissioned on September 11, 1843.

In 1970, the lighthouse was taken over by the provincial government and developed as a historic site. The building has been returned to its condition in the 1870s, being painted with dramatic red and white stripes that make it clearly visible in daylight. The lantern room contains a rare catoptric light that dates from 1816 (when first commissioned, the lighthouse employed a secondhand light from a lighthouse in Scotland). This has 18in (46cm) silver and copper reflectors, brass oil lamps, and an iron mounting. This type of light required a lot of attention to operate effectively—the keeper could not afford to allow any of the lamps to go out during the night, and he had to rotate them by means of a handcrank. In the morning, the wicks would have to be trimmed, the lamps filled, and the reflectors polished.

Far left: *The basis for the structure is a 36ft (11m) high, round stone tower with a lantern and gallery. This rises from the center of a square, two-story wooden keeper's house. The lighthouse remained in operation until 1966, when the light was transferred to a skeletal steel tower nearby.*

Top right: *The lighthouse, with the exception of the tower and light room, has been restored to its condition in the 1870s. The living quarters are furnished and decorated as they would have been when Jeremiah White, the lightkeeper at 80 years of age, was in residence, along with his family, assisted by son Nicholas.*

Right: *From its perch high on the rocky coastline, the power of the North Atlantic crashing against the rocks can be witnessed. From this vantage point it is possible to see icebergs, and whales and puffins congregate just off the cape.*

LIGHTNING STRIKE

During a storm on August 3, 2001, lightning struck the Cape Bonavista Lighthouse three times, setting the building on fire. At the time, the lighthouse was undergoing restoration and, fortunately, all the museum's valuable artifacts had been removed. Although the electrical system was destroyed and extensive damage was caused to the second floor, sufficient decorative details were saved to enable the restoration to continue.

Cape Bonavista, Newfoundland, Canada

Fogo Island

Cape Bonavista Lighthouse, Cape Bonavista

Gander

NEWFOUNDLAND

King's Cove

Grates Cove

St. John's

Lime Kiln Lighthouse

San Juan Island, Washington, USA

• **Lime Kiln Lighthouse stands on San Juan Island facing Vancouver Island across the Haro Strait. The building takes its name from the remains of nearby lime kilns that date from the late nineteenth century.**

• **The lighthouse was the last major nautical light established in the State of Washington and the last to receive electricity.**

• **Although the lighthouse is still in operation as an aid to navigation, the fog signal building from which it rises is now a whale research station.**

The San Juan Islands form an archipelago at the southern end of the Strait of Georgia, between the mainland of Washington and Canada's Vancouver Island. The largest of the group is San Juan Island itself. When Britain and the United States finally settled their dispute over the Oregon Territory (which included Washington State) in 1846, the international border was set to the east of the Strait of Georgia. However, this did not clarify the status of the San Juan Islands, which led to further dispute, culminating in a military stalemate known as the Pig War. Eventually, the border was established in the Haro Strait in 1872, after the German Kaiser, Wilhelm I, acted as arbitrator. Today, the strait is a major waterway for shipping on their way to the port of Vancouver from the Pacific Ocean.

Lime Kiln Lighthouse was erected on the western coast of San Juan Island in Dead Man's Bay, close to the town of Friday Harbor. The light station itself was established in 1914, but the present 38ft (12m) high, octagonal concrete tower was not built until five years later. It first began operating on June 30, 1919. An electricity supply was not laid on until the late 1940s.

The lighthouse was manned until 1962, when it was fully automated, photoelectric cells being used to switch the light on and off in response to changing daylight levels. The original wooden keepers' dwellings, set back from the lighthouse among the trees, are used to house rangers for Lime Kiln Point State Park.

Far left: *On a clear day, Lime Kiln Lighthouse offers a commanding view of the Olympic Mountain range and the shores of Vancouver Island. On most days, however, it is misty and visibility limited.*

Top right: *The elegant octagonal tower rises from one end of a square, single-story, former fog signal building. The tower supports a gallery and lantern, which was equipped originally with a fourth-order Fresnel lens. The modern optic flashes a white light once every ten seconds.*

Right: *Sitting on the rocky shore of the island at a height of 55ft (16.7m), the beacon is visible from a distance of 17 miles (27km). The Fresnel lens was replaced in 1998 with an aerobeacon, which, originally designed for use in airports, became widely used in lighthouses throughout the United States from the 1950s.*

WHALE SANCTUARY

In 1985, the Lime Kiln Lighthouse and the surrounding area of sea were dedicated as a whale sanctuary and research station. The former fog signal building was taken over by the Whale Museum, and fitted with webcams and hydrophone equipment so that scientists could monitor the movements of orca whales in the Haro Strait.

San Juan Island, Washington, USA

Vancouver •

Saanich •

Seattle •

Spokane •

Lime Kiln Lighthouse, San Juan Island

Kennewick •

Märket Lighthouse

Märket Island, Finland

• **The charming lighthouse that stands on the uninhabited island of Märket in the Sea of Åland is the westernmost building in Finland.**

• **Built in the late nineteenth century, the lighthouse continues to guide ships on their way between the Baltic Sea and Gulf of Bothnia, which separates Finland and Sweden.**

• **The lighthouse is famous for being at the center of an international border anomaly that lasted for almost a hundred years.**

Off the southwestern tip of Finland, between the Baltic Sea and the Gulf of Bothnia, lie the Åland Islands, an archipelago comprising the main island of Fasta Åland and thousands of smaller islands. This maze of islands has always been an obstacle to shipping in the region, and lighthouses abound. One of the most interesting is the Märket Lighthouse, not necessarily because of its age or architectural qualities, but because its location led to an exchange of territory between Finland and Sweden.

The island of Märket lies about 19 miles (30km) to the west of Fasta Åland and is tiny, measuring only about 1,150ft (350m) long by 490ft (150m) wide. It is low lying, too, standing little more than 10ft (3m) above the waves, which often made it difficult to see in the years before the lighthouse was built. Consequently, it gained a fearsome reputation among local seafarers.

In 1885, the lighthouse was erected on Märket, having been designed by a Finnish architect by the name of Georg Schreck. It has an octagonal stone tower, with a gallery and lantern, that rises from the roof of a two-story keeper's house, also built of stone. The tower itself stands 46ft (14m) high, while the entire building is painted with red and white horizontal stripes to make it more visible. The lantern displays a flashing white light, which has been operated automatically since 1979.

In 1809, when Sweden relinquished sovereignty over Finland to the Russian Empire, it was decided that the international border would run through Märket, the channel to the west being Swedish, while the strait to the east would be Russian. When the lighthouse was erected by the Russian administration, the builders chose the highest point on the island without realizing that it was in Swedish territory. Since the island was uninhabited, this caused no real problems, and for decades first Russia, then Finland, operated the lighthouse on foreign soil. Eventually, in 1981, Sweden and Finland signed a treaty that eliminated the anomaly. The area around the light station was transferred to Finland in return for an equal amount of Finnish land. To achieve this, it was necessary to redraw the border, which now zigzags across the island in a reverse "S" shape.

RADIO STATION

The Finnish half of Märket is of particular interest to amateur radio enthusiasts, who regard it as a separate country. It has its own callsign prefix, and regular radio expeditions are made to the island from where contacts are made with radio amateurs around the world.

Far left: *After Märket Lighthouse had been left unmanned in 1976, the Finnish Lighthouse Society, founded to promote protection and preservation of Finnish lighthouses, rented it in 2007, and manned it the summer of that year, and the year after. The fascinating diaries of the lighthouse keepers are available from the lighthouse's website (see Acknowledgments).*

Top right: *Renovation of the lighthouse and its ancillary buildings is under way, with total restoration anticipated for the jubilee celebrations in 2010. The FLS plans to raise the money necessary by attracting visitors to the isolated spot.*

Right: *The zigzag border between Sweden and Finland was drawn on the rock that forms the island to highlight the previous anomaly, which had left the little lighthouse on the Swedish side for 96 years.*

Märket Island, Finland

Märket Lighthouse, Märket Island

Hudiksvall •

Gulf of Bothnia

FINLAND

• Turku

Gävle •

Östhammar •

SWEDEN

• Stockholm

New London Ledge Lighthouse

Connecticut, USA

- **The stately New London Ledge Lighthouse, at the entrance to New London Harbor in Long Island Sound, is unusual for having been built in the architectural style of the French Second Empire.**

- **The lighthouse was constructed in the early twentieth century and was one of the last to be erected in New England. It remains in operation as a guide to navigation.**

- **It is said that the lighthouse is haunted by the ghost of a former keeper.**

The harbor of New London, in Connecticut, sits at the mouth of the Thames River, which empties into the eastern end of Long Island Sound. The port was developed originally as a whaling center, but by the early twentieth century, it had become an industrial city and maritime commerce had grown substantially.

One of the problems faced by vessels entering the port was that they had to navigate their way around dangerous ledges that lie just beneath the surface of the sea at the entrance to the harbor. A lighthouse had been erected in the harbor itself, but this was considered inadequate to ensure the safety of shipping, so another was planned for the entrance.

Located on the Southwest Ledge, the lighthouse was constructed by the Hamilton R. Douglas Company of New London, being completed in 1909. The elegant building stands on a concrete caisson that was towed to the site, filled with concrete and crushed rock, and sunk in 28ft (8.5m) of water.

The lighthouse was manned until 1987, when the light was automated. Today, the building has been taken over by the New London Ledge Lighthouse Foundation, whose aim is to renovate the structure and open it to the public as a museum and bed and breakfast accommodation.

Far left: *It is said that the distinctive French Second Empire styling of New London Ledge Lighthouse was influenced by wealthy homeowners on the adjacent coast, who wanted a structure that would reflect the elegance of their properties.*

Top right: *The resulting building was a square, two-story, brick keeper's house with a mansard roof, dormer windows, and granite detailing.*

Right: *Rising from the center of the roof is a round gallery and cast-iron lantern. The building stands on a concrete caisson above which is a square concrete pier containing a cellar and water tanks.*

GHOSTLY ANTICS

A famous ghost story surrounds the New London Ledge Lighthouse. It is said that sometime in the 1920s or 1930s, a keeper by the name of Ernie either jumped or fell to his death from the lighthouse roof after learning that his wife had run off with a ferryboat captain. Subsequently, his ghost returned to haunt the building, causing mischief by opening and closing doors, operating the fog signal, and freeing securely moored boats among other things. Various attempts have been made to verify the tale, and some strange activities have been recorded, but whether they were caused by Ernie or more natural phenomena has not been established.

New Holland Harbor, Connecticut, USA

Hartford •
Providence •
New Haven •
New London • • Groton
Bridgeport •
• New York

New London Ledge Lighthouse, New Holland Harbor

Kjeungskjaer Lighthouse

Trondheim, Norway

- **Kjeungskjaer Lighthouse marks an area of dangerous rocky outcrops near the entrance of Bjugn Fjord, not far from Trondheim, on the Norwegian coast.**

- **Dating from the late nineteenth century, the unusual-looking, integral lighthouse dwarfs the tiny and low islet on which it stands.**

- **Although still an active aid to navigation, the lighthouse has not been manned for twenty years.**

The mountainous coast of Norway is a rugged and rocky place, deeply incised with flooded valleys known as fjords, and with a barrier of small islands and reefs that lies offshore for practically its entire length. Navigating a vessel through these islands is fraught with danger, so nautical lights have a really important role to play in ensuring the safety of mariners in this region. As many as 212 lighthouses have been built along the Norwegian coast, although not all of them were operational at the same time.

To the west of the city of Trondheim and the massive Trondheim Fjord, lies the smaller Bjugn Fjord where the local community relies very much on the sea for a living, since herring fishing plays a major part in the economy. With fishing boats coming and going constantly, marking the dangerous rocks at the entrance to the fjord is vital. To help with this task, the Kjeungskjaer Lighthouse was erected on a low-lying, rocky islet about 2 miles (3km) to the west of the harbor of Uthaug.

Unusually for a Norwegian lighthouse, Kjeungskjaer is of an integral design. A three-story, octagonal, stone dwelling was built with a lantern and gallery that rise from the roof of the building. The lantern itself was equipped originally with French optical apparatus, although this is no longer in use, a more modern beacon being installed. This flashes white, red, or green, depending on the direction from which it is viewed. The lighthouse stands 56ft (17m) high and dominates the surrounding seascape. The light was commissioned in 1880, the tower being manned until 1987, when the light was automated.

Far left: *Kjeungskjaer Lighthouse makes an unusual sight among the rugged islands that dot this area of the Norwegian coast. Standing on a low, rocky islet, the brick-red building with its roof-mounted lantern appears to be marooned, the last remnant of some long-lost town that has been swallowed up by the waves.*

Top right: *The sturdy tower has withstood the harsh weather conditions that prevail in this part of the world for almost 130 years, making a major contribution to safe navigation in these dangerous waters.*

Right: *As night falls and the mist rolls in, Kjeungskjaer Lighthouse stands ready to send its warning light across the dark sea, marking the rocks that can spell doom to unwary mariners.*

Trondheim, Norway

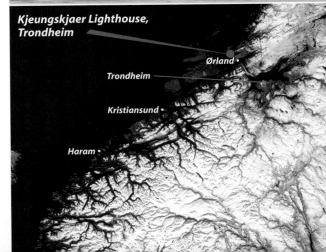

Kjeungskjaer Lighthouse, Trondheim

Ørland

Trondheim

Kristiansund

Haram

LIGHTHOUSE VACATION

Although not perhaps to everyone's taste, the Kjeungskjaer Lighthouse makes for an unusual—and very peaceful—place to stay on vacation. The keepers' quarters, no longer used since the light was automated, include an apartment suitable for up to six guests.

153

Sandy Point Shoal Lighthouse

Maryland, USA

- Sandy Point Shoal Lighthouse marks an area of dangerous shoals in the upper reaches of Chesapeake Bay on the east coast of the United States.
- Built in the late nineteenth century, the distinctive, Empire-style lighthouse continues to guide shipping on its way up the Chesapeake to the port of Baltimore.
- Today, the lighthouse is privately owned, having been offered for sale on an internet auction site. However, the U.S. Coast Guard remains responsible for maintenance of the light.

The present lighthouse is not the first to mark the treacherous shoals off Sandy Point. In 1858, a building incorporating keeper's quarters and an integral tower was erected onshore on the western bank of the Chesapeake, close to where the modern suspension bridge stands. It soon became clear, however, that this lighthouse was far from adequate, particularly during stormy weather. The shoals extended a mile (1.6km) from shore, and the poor light displayed by the lighthouse was of little use to vessels drawing more than 10ft (3m). Furthermore, the fog bell often could not be heard. By the 1870s, traffic in the bay had increased considerably with many large passenger steamers making their way toward Baltimore.

The Lighthouse Board wanted to erect a screwpile lighthouse on the shoals, but Congress would not allocate sufficient funds, so instead a caisson design was chosen. Work began on this in August 1883, and by the end of October that year the light was operational. The cast-iron caisson was assembled and sunk into a 3ft (1m) excavation in the sand, then filled with concrete to weigh it down.

The caisson was topped with a two-story, brick keeper's dwelling measuring 24ft (7.3m) square and built in Empire style. The corners of the building are truncated, giving it an octagonal appearance. The mansard roof has dormer windows, and supports a gallery and lantern. The first two floors of the building were used as living quarters, while the roof housed the watchroom. A cellar in the caisson provided storage for coal, oil, and water. The lighthouse was manned until 1963, when it was automated. Today, the lantern houses a solar-powered, electric light.

Far left: *Standing in open water just north of the Chesapeake Bay Bridge, Sandy Point Shoal Lighthouse, despite frequent renovation, suffered deterioration and mindless vandalism until it was sold to a private bidder in an internet auction. Only time will tell whether this fine example of the important offshore lighthouses will regain its former stature.*

Top right: *Despite efforts to maintain the building, the lower gallery deck was badly cracked and threatened to admit water between the concrete and iron parts of the caisson. The Coast Guard removed deteriorating tin cornices and replaced them with matching mahogany components.*

Right: *A new copper roof was added in 1995, while the unmanned lighthouse became the home of squatters in 2006, in the form of ospreys nesting on the lantern gallery.*

Chesapeake Bay, Maryland, USA

Sandy Point Shoal Lighthouse, Chesapeake Bay

- Baltimore
- Annapolis
- Washington
- Deale
- Easton
- Fredericksburg

VANDALIZATION, AND A NEW OWNER

In 1979, vandals broke into Sandy Point Shoal Lighthouse and broke most of the windows in the lantern. Worse, they smashed the priceless, nineteenth-century, Fresnel crystal lens. Although a reward was offered for information that would lead to their apprehension, no one was ever caught.

Because of escalating maintenance costs, the lighthouse was offered for disposal in 2004 under the National Historic Lighthouse Preservation Act, but no non-profit organization came forward to take on the historic building. Subsequently, in 2006, it was offered on the internet auction site eBay, where it sold to a private individual for $250,000.

Kiz Kulesi Lighthouse

Istanbul, Turkey

- Kiz Kulesi Lighthouse stands on a tiny islet in the southern entrance to the Bosporus Strait, which separates the European and Asian halves of the Turkish city of Istanbul.
- The lighthouse is also known as the Maiden's Tower and Leander's Tower, and there are various legends to explain these names.
- The building has had many roles throughout its life, and although no longer active as an aid to navigation, it remains a symbol of the city and a major tourist attraction.

The narrow strait known as the Bosporus connects the Sea of Marmara with the Black Sea and forms part of an important waterway between the latter and the Mediterranean. Straddling the Bosporus is the city of Istanbul, half in Asia and half in Europe. One of the most historic and well-known structures in the city is Kiz Kulesi, a square stone tower with an octagonal upper story that rises from a fortified building on a tiny islet in the middle of the Bosporus.

The present tower was built in the eighteenth century, but the island has been the site of many important structures over the centuries. The first was a fortress built by the Athenian general Alcibiades in 408 BC. Another fortress was erected in 1110 by Alexius Comnenus. A lighthouse was recorded on the island in the early sixteenth century, and the tower's present form dates from 1763, when the Ottoman emperor Mustafa III had it rebuilt. In addition to being used as a lighthouse, it has seen service as a watchtower, a prison, a customs post, and a home for retired naval officers. Today, the buildings contain a restaurant, a museum, gift shop, and an observation platform.

Far left: *One of the most romantic symbols of Istanbul, Kiz Kulesi Lighthouse—no longer a guide for vessels in the strait—is illuminated sympathetically at night in its modern transformation as a tourist attraction.*

Top right: *The attendant buildings, once fortified against attackers, now fulfill a more peaceful role, including a picturesque outdoor restaurant beneath the ornate tower.*

Right: *Elegant and stately, Kiz Kulesi Lighthouse and its surrounding buildings occupy most of the tiny islet. Frequent boats ferry tourists to and from Kabatas, Ortaköy, and Salacak.*

Istanbul, Turkey

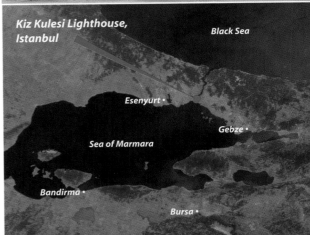

Kiz Kulesi Lighthouse, Istanbul

Black Sea

Esenyurt

Gebze

Sea of Marmara

Bandirma

Bursa

NAMES OF LEGEND

A variety of legends have grown up around Kiz Kulesi Lighthouse, explaining its alternative names. The oldest is the Greek story of Leander and Hero. It is said that Hero lived on the tiny island and that Leander would swim the strait each day to meet with her. One day the waves overcame him and he died. Grief-stricken, Hero committed suicide. Thus, the building is known as Leander's Tower. However, this story is also said to apply to a site in the Dardanelles, farther to the west. Another explanation for the Leander's Tower name is that a Byzantine emperor became angry when he learned that his daughter, Leander, was having a love affair. He ordered that the tower be constructed and imprisoned his daughter there.

The most well-known of the legends is that the Emperor Constantine had the tower built for his daughter. It had been predicted that she would die from a snake bite. Knowing that the island had no snakes, Constantine sent his beloved daughter there, but to no avail. She was bitten by a snake that had arrived in a basket of grapes. Ever after, the tower was known as the Maiden's Tower (Kiz Kulesi in Turkish).

INDEX

ACKNOWLEDGMENTS

Corbis: Cover, main, bottom right; 9 top; 12; 23 top; 25 bottom; 42; 45 top; 46; 48; 49 top, bottom; 54; 61 top; 99 top, bottom; 102; 103 bottom; 104; 109 top; 111 top; 116; 119 bottom; 140; 141 top, bottom; 145 bottom; 147 top, bottom; 153 bottom; 156.

Getty Images: 13 bottom; 14; 21 bottom; 23 bottom; 24; 28; 34; 37 bottom; 50; 55 bottom; 56; 60; 68; 69 top; 71 top; 83 bottom; 86; 92; 98; 121 top; 124; 125 top; 129 bottom; 150; 157 bottom.

Photolibrary: Cover bottom left, back, spine; 6; 7 bottom; 8; 18; 20; 21 top; 22; 30; 31 bottom; 32; 33 bottom; 38; 39 top; 40; 41 bottom; 43 top; 44; 62; 63 top, bottom; 70; 71 bottom; 76; 77 top, bottom; 80; 81 top, bottom; 82; 88; 93 top, bottom; 94; 96; 105 bottom; 108; 118; 120; 121 bottom; 122; 123 top; 125 bottom; 126; 130; 131 top, bottom; 136; 137 top, bottom; 146; 152.

iStockphoto: 7 right/John Steele, center right/Daniel Loiselle; 9 bottom/Stéphane Bidouze; 13 top/Black Beck Photographic; 15 top/Alohaspirit; 19 top/Heizfrosch, bottom/Darren deans; 26/Steve Stone; 29 bottom/Sublimation; 35 bottom/Harvey Silikovitz; 41 top/Holger Franke; 45 top/Adrian beesley; 47 top/Andrew Ma, bottom/Dan Cooper; 51 top/Micheal O'Fiachra, bottom/Brian Kelly; 57 top/Cornelia Togea; 64, 65 bottom/David Pedre; 78, 79 top/Andrew Penner; 79 bottom/Denis Tangney; 83 top/Thomas Görick; 84/Drosera; 85 bottom/Alohaspirit; 87 top/Derk Hayenga; 89 top/Dean Turner, bottom/David Freund; 91 top/Doug Ransom, bottom/Norman Pogson; 95 bottom/Rest; 101 top/ArsMaior, bottom/Peter Zaharov; 103 top/Sally Scott; 109 bottom/Roxana Gonzalez; 110/Frank Boellmann; 111 bottom/Jonathan Larsen; 117 top/Michael Westhoff; 127 top/Iris Millikan, bottom/Gary Unwin; 128/Jeff Gynane; 133 bottom/Nicholas Sereno; 134/Irina Korshunova; 138/Albert Barr; 139 top/Robert Goldberg, bottom/Michael Bagley; 142/Mark Coffey; 143 top/Luan Tran, bottom/Catnap72; 144, 145 top/Gina Smith; 151 bottom/Kenneth C. Zirkel; 157 top/Bulent Ince.

Fotolia: 4/Delepine Antony; 10/Antoine; 11 top, bottom/Bruno Delacotte; 35 top/Olivier; 43 bottom/Chee-Onn Leong; 53 top/Riccardo Arata; 61 bottom/Philippe Perraud; 74/Philip Lange; 75 bottom/Ernst-P; 85 top/Jonie; 87 bottom/Almuth Becker; 90/Norman Pogson; 95 top/Wjarek; 97 top/Vanessa martineau, bottom/Carabay; 100/SDuggan; 105 top/Christopher Meder; 106/PP-Photo; 107 top/Jo Chambers, bottom/Joerg Humpe; 114/Armin Sepp; 119 top/Wolfgang Jargstorff; 129 top/Pix by Marti; 132/fnalphotos.com; 133/Aidas Zubkonis; 153 top/Forcdan.

Wikimedia Commons: 7/Henrik Jessen; 15 bottom/Jean-Baptiste Fagot; 17 top/Benjamin Evans, bottom; 31 top/Kubigula; 33 top/Jürgen Howaldt; 52/Alessandro Cai; 53 bottom/Rinina25; 58/Andrew Phillips; 59 top/Jimmy S. Emerson, bottom/Andrew Phillips; 65 top/Arturo Nikolai; 67 bottom/Magma; 69 bottom/Tor Svensson; 73 bottom/Herwig Reidlinger; 75 top/Steinbach; 117 bottom/TYC; 123 bottom/Rüdiger Wölk; 151 top/Kevin Pepin.

Anssi Koskinen: Cover, bottom centre.
Rick Payne: 16.
Robert English: 25 top; 155 top.
Bruce & Carmel: 27 top, bottom.
Jordi Bosh Diez: 29 top.
Jacqueline Savitz: 36.
Lisa Egeli: 37 top.
Daisuke Watanabe: 39 top.
Zorglub: 55 top.
Daniel Cartwright: 57 bottom.
Anssi Koskinen: 66; 67 top.
Giancarlo Massario: 72; 73 top.
Wilson Marin & Bengtskär Ltd: 112, 113 top/Jarmo Vehkakoski, bottom/Kajus Hedenström.
Cyrus Farivar: 115 top, bottom.
Alexander Zubov: 135 top.
Khaosaming: 135 bottom.
www.lighthousesociety.fi: 148; 149 top, bottom/Pekka Väisänen
Ulis Fleming: 154.
Cathy T: 155 bottom.

NASA Visible Earth: All satellite images.